GRADE 3

Curriculum Units

How Many Hundreds? How Many Miles?

Addition, Subtraction, and the Number System 3

UNIT 8

Ikenaga 2 Jos Leys

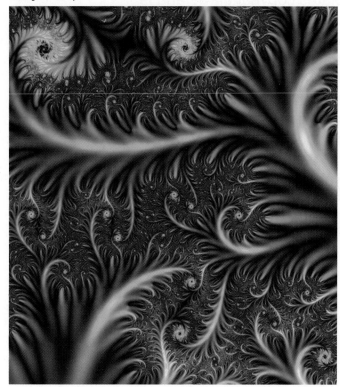

"A relatively simple formula can generate immensely complex images." – **Jos Leys**

Investigations

IN NUMBER, DATA, AND SPACE®

Glenview, Illinois • Boston, Massachusetts
Chandler, Arizona • Upper Saddle River, New Jersey

The Investigations curriculum was developed by TERC, Cambridge, MA.

This material is based on work supported by the National Science Foundation ("NSF") under Grant No. ESI-0095450. Any opinions, findings, and conclusions or recommendations expressed in this material are those of the author(s) and do not necessarily reflect the views of the National Science Foundation.

ISBN-13: 978-0-328-60027-4

ISBN-10: 0-328-60027-X

T E R C

Co-Principal Investigators

Susan Jo Russell

Karen Economopoulos

Authors

Lucy Wittenberg
Director Grades 3–5

Karen Economopoulos
Director Grades K–2

Virginia Bastable
(SummerMath for Teachers,
Mt. Holyoke College)

Katie Hickey Bloomfield

Keith Cochran

Darrell Earnest

Arusha Hollister

Nancy Horowitz

Erin Leidl

Megan Murray

Young Oh

Beth W. Perry

Susan Jo Russell

Deborah Schifter
(Education
Development Center)

Kathy Sillman

Administrative Staff

Amy Taber
Project Manager

Beth Bergeron

Lorraine Brooks

Emi Fujiwara

Contributing Authors

Denise Baumann

Jennifer DiBrienza

Hollee Freeman

Paula Hooper

Jan Mokros

Stephen Monk
(University of Washington)

Mary Beth O'Connor

Judy Storeygard

Cornelia Tierney

Elizabeth Van Cleef

Carol Wright

Technology

Jim Hammerman

Classroom Field Work

Amy Appell

Rachel E. Davis

Traci Higgins

Julia Thompson

Collaborating Teachers

This group of dedicated teachers carried out extensive field testing in their classrooms, met regularly to discuss issues of teaching and learning mathematics, provided feedback to staff, welcomed staff into their classrooms to document students' work, and contributed both suggestions and written material that has been incorporated into the curriculum.

Bethany Altchek

Linda Amaral

Kimberly Beauregard

Barbara Bernard

Nancy Buell

Rose Christiansen

Chris Colbath-Hess

Lisette Colon

Kim Cook

Frances Cooper

Kathleen Drew

Rebeka Eston Salemi

Thomas Fisher

Michael Flynn

Holly Ghazey

Susan Gillis

Danielle Harrington

Elaine Herzog

Francine Hiller

Kirsten Lee Howard

Liliana Klass

Leslie Kramer

Melissa Lee Andrichak

Kelley Lee Sadowski

Jennifer Levitan

Mary Lou LoVecchio

Kristen McEnaney

Maura McGrail

Kathe Millett

Florence Molyneaux

Amy Monkiewicz

Elizabeth Monopoli

Carol Murray

Robyn Musser

Christine Norrman

Deborah O'Brien

Timothy O'Connor

Anne Marie O'Reilly

Mark Paige

Margaret Riddle

Karen Schweitzer

Elisabeth Seyferth

Susan Smith

Debra Sorvillo

Shoshanah Starr

Janice Szymaszek

Karen Tobin

JoAnn Trauschke

Ana Vaisenstein

Yvonne Watson

Michelle Woods

Mary Wright

Note: Unless otherwise noted, all contributors listed above were staff of the Education Research Collaborative at TERC during their work on the curriculum. Other affiliations during the time of development are listed.

Advisors

Deborah Lowenberg Ball,
University of Michigan

Hyman Bass, Professor of Mathematics and Mathematics Education
University of Michigan

Mary Canner, Principal, Natick Public Schools

Thomas Carpenter, Professor of Curriculum and Instruction,
University of Wisconsin-Madison

Janis Freckmann, Elementary Mathematics Coordinator,
Milwaukee Public Schools

Lynne Godfrey, Mathematics Coach,
Cambridge Public Schools

Ginger Hanlon, Instructional Specialist in Mathematics,
New York City Public Schools

DeAnn Huinker, Director, Center for Mathematics and
Science Education Research, University of Wisconsin-Milwaukee

James Kaput, Professor of Mathematics, University of
Massachusetts-Dartmouth

Kate Kline, Associate Professor, Department of Mathematics
and Statistics, Western Michigan University

Jim Lewis, Professor of Mathematics,
University of Nebraska-Lincoln

William McCallum, Professor of Mathematics,
University of Arizona

Harriet Pollatsek, Professor of Mathematics,
Mount Holyoke College

Debra Shein-Gerson, Elementary Mathematics Specialist,
Weston Public Schools

Gary Shevell, Assistant Principal,
New York City Public Schools

Liz Sweeney, Elementary Math Department,
Boston Public Schools

Lucy West, Consultant, Metamorphosis:
Teaching Learning Communities, Inc.

This revision of the curriculum was built on the work of the many authors who contributed to the first edition (published between 1994 and 1998). We acknowledge the critical contributions of these authors in developing the content and pedagogy of *Investigations*:

Authors

Joan Akers

Michael T. Battista

Douglas H. Clements

Karen Economopoulos

Marlene Kliman

Jan Mokros

Megan Murray

Ricardo Nemirovsky

Andee Rubin

Susan Jo Russell

Cornelia Tierney

Contributing Authors

Mary Berle-Carman

Rebecca B. Corwin

Rebeka Eston

Claryce Evans

Anne Goodrow

Cliff Konold

Chris Mainhart

Sue McMillen

Jerrie Moffet

Tracy Noble

Kim O'Neil

Mark Ogonowski

Julie Sarama

Amy Shulman Weinberg

Margie Singer

Virginia Woolley

Tracey Wright

Contents

UNIT 8

How Many Hundreds? How Many Miles?

Investigations

CURRICULUM

Overview of Program Components

The **Curriculum Units** are the teaching guides. (See far right.)

Implementing Investigations in Grade 3 offers suggestions for implementing the curriculum. It also contains a comprehensive index.

The **Differentiation and Intervention Guide** offers additional activities for each Investigation to support the range of learners.

Investigations for the Interactive Whiteboard provides whole-class instructional support to enhance each session.

The **Resource Masters and Transparencies CD** contains all reproducible materials that support instruction. The **LogoPaths CD** provides an environment in which students investigate a variety of geometric ideas.

The **Student Activity Book** contains the consumable student pages (Recording Sheets, Homework, Practice, and so on).

The **Student Math Handbook** contains Math Words and Ideas pages and Games directions.

The *Investigations* Curriculum

Investigations in Number, Data, and Space® is a K–5 mathematics curriculum designed to engage students in making sense of mathematical ideas. Six major goals guided the development of the *Investigations in Number, Data, and Space®* curriculum. The curriculum is designed to:

- Support students to make sense of mathematics and learn that they can be mathematical thinkers

- Focus on computational fluency with whole numbers as a major goal of the elementary grades

- Provide substantive work in important areas of mathematics—rational numbers, geometry, measurement, data, and early algebra—and connections among them

- Emphasize reasoning about mathematical ideas

- Communicate mathematics content and pedagogy to teachers

- Engage the range of learners in understanding mathematics

Underlying these goals are three guiding principles that are touchstones for the *Investigations* team as we approach both students and teachers as agents of their own learning:

1. *Students have mathematical ideas.* Students come to school with ideas about numbers, shapes, measurements, patterns, and data. If given the opportunity to learn in an environment that stresses making sense of mathematics, students build on the ideas they already have and learn about new mathematics they have never encountered. Students learn that they are capable of having mathematical ideas, applying what they know to new situations, and thinking and reasoning about unfamiliar problems.

2. *Teachers are engaged in ongoing learning* about mathematics content, pedagogy, and student learning. The curriculum provides material for professional development, to be used by teachers individually or in groups, that supports teachers' continued learning as they use the curriculum over several years. The *Investigations* curriculum materials are designed as much to be a dialogue with teachers as to be a core of content for students.

3. *Teachers collaborate with the students and curriculum materials* to create the curriculum as enacted in the classroom. The only way for a good curriculum to be used well is for teachers to be active participants in implementing it. Teachers use the curriculum to maintain a clear, focused, and coherent agenda for mathematics teaching. At the same time, they observe and listen carefully to students, try to understand how they are thinking, and make teaching decisions based on these observations.

Investigations is based on experience from research and practice, including field testing that involved documentation of thousands of hours in classrooms, observations of students, input from teachers, and analysis of student work. As a result, the curriculum addresses the learning needs of real students in a wide range of classrooms and communities. The investigations are carefully designed to invite all students into mathematics—girls and boys; members of diverse cultural, ethnic, and language groups; and students with a wide variety of strengths, needs, and interests.

Based on this extensive classroom testing, the curriculum takes seriously the time students need to develop a strong conceptual foundation and skills based on that foundation. Each curriculum unit focuses on an area of content in depth, providing time for students to develop and practice ideas across a variety of activities and contexts that build on each other. Daily guidelines for time spent on class sessions, Classroom Routines (K–3), and Ten-Minute Math (3–5) reflect the commitment to devoting adequate time to mathematics in each school day.

About This Curriculum Unit

This **Curriculum Unit** is one of nine teaching guides in Grade 3. The eighth unit in Grade 3 is *How Many Hundreds? How Many Miles?*

- The **Introduction and Overview** section organizes and presents the instructional materials, provides background information, and highlights important features specific to this unit.

- Each Curriculum Unit contains several **Investigations.** Each Investigation focuses on a set of related mathematical ideas.

- Investigations are divided into one-hour **Sessions,** or lessons.

- Sessions have a combination of these parts: **Activity, Discussion, Math Workshop, Assessment Activity,** and **Session Follow-Up.**

- Each session also has one or more **Classroom Routines and Ten-Minute Math** activities that are done outside of math time.

- At the back of the book is a collection of **Teacher Notes** and **Dialogue Boxes** that provide professional development related to the unit.

- Also included at the back of the book are the **Student Math Handbook** pages for this unit.

- The **Index** provides a way to look up important words or terms.

Overview

O F   T H I S   U N I T

Each *Investigations* session has some combination of these five parts: **Activity, Discussion, Math Workshop, Assessment Activity,** and **Session Follow-Up.** These session parts are indicated in the chart below. Each session also has one **Classroom Routine or Ten-Minute Math** activity that is done outside of math time.

 Ⓦ Interactive Whiteboard

Activity	Discussion	Math Workshop	Assessment Activity	Session Follow-Up	Counting Around the Class	Guess My Rule
●Ⓦ●				●	Ⓦ	
Ⓦ		●		●	Ⓦ	
	Ⓦ	●		●	Ⓦ	
	Ⓦ	●	●	●	Ⓦ	
	Ⓦ	●	●	●	Ⓦ	
●	Ⓦ●			●		Ⓦ
Ⓦ●	●			●		Ⓦ
●	●			●		Ⓦ
●		Ⓦ		●		Ⓦ
	Ⓦ	●	●	●		Ⓦ
Ⓦ●	Ⓦ			●	Ⓦ	
●	Ⓦ			●	Ⓦ	
●	Ⓦ		●	●	Ⓦ	
	Ⓦ	●	●	●	Ⓦ	
	Ⓦ	●		●		Ⓦ
●	●			●		Ⓦ
Ⓦ		●		●		Ⓦ
	Ⓦ	●		●		Ⓦ
			●	●		Ⓦ

Mathematics

How Many Hundreds? How Many Miles?, which focuses on the operations of addition and subtraction, is the fourth Grade 3 unit in the number and operations strand of *Investigations.* These units develop ideas about the meaning of operations with whole numbers, the development of computational fluency, the structure of place value and the base-ten number system, and generalizations about numbers and operations.

LOOKING BACK The work of this unit assumes that students bring with them an understanding of, and the ability to solve, addition and subtraction problems with 2- and 3-digit numbers under 400. It is also expected that they know addition combinations to 10 + 10 fluently and can use these to solve both addition and subtraction problems. In a previous addition and subtraction unit in Grade 3, *Collections and Travel Stories,* students extended their understanding of the base-ten structure of our number system to 3-digit numbers by examining the structure of numbers to 1,000. They continued to develop their computational fluency by adding and subtracting multiples of 10 and practicing strategies for addition and subtraction with 3-digit numbers. Their work in subtraction also focused on understanding different types of subtraction problems, including comparison, removal, and finding a missing part.

This unit focuses on 2 Mathematical Emphases:

1 Computational Fluency Adding and subtracting accurately and efficiently

Math Focus Points

- Combining hundreds to numbers above 1,000

- Subtracting from multiples of 100

- Adding multiples of 10 and 100 to, and subtracting them from, 3-digit numbers

- Estimating answers to subtraction problems with 3-digit numbers

- Using the relationship of numbers in a subtraction expression to multiples of 100 to solve subtraction problems

- Solving addition problems with 3-digit numbers

- Estimating and solving addition problems with sums greater than 1,000

- Solving addition problems with more than 2 addends

- Estimating which of two sums is greater

- Knowing and using subtraction problems related to the addition combinations to 10 + 10 (the subtraction facts, e.g., 8 − 5, 13 − 9) with fluency

- Solving addition and subtraction problems in the context of money (dollars, cents)

- Determining combinations of addends for a given sum

- Solving addition and subtraction problems with more than one step

In this unit, students continue to develop fluency with addition and subtraction of numbers in the hundreds. For third graders, working with numbers this large can be challenging because it is more difficult to grasp the magnitude of the quantities. Third graders do not deal frequently with quantities like 730, and when they do hear them (e.g., there are 730 students in the school, 730 days in two years, 730 people in the auditorium for the play), they may not realize how large those quantities are. Developing ways to think about and estimate with numbers of this size is critical for computation with multidigit numbers. Otherwise, students can easily follow the steps of computational procedures but lose track of the meaning of the quantities. Then, when they make errors—as we all do—they do not notice that the result of their computation is not reasonable, given the quantities in the problem.

One way students learn to make estimates in this unit is by focusing on the largest part of the quantities. For example, when we add 623 and 249, how many hundreds will be in the sum? How many hundreds will be in the sum when we add 623 and 289? Students pay attention to the meaning of the digit in the hundreds place of each number (600 + 200), as well as the digit in the tens place of each number (20 + 40 in the first sum, 20 + 80 in the second sum), to estimate the number of hundreds in the sum. Students also notice which "landmark numbers"—usually multiples of 10—are close to the numbers they are working with: 623 + 249 is close to 620 + 250, so the sum will be very close to 870.

Throughout this unit, encourage students to add parts of the numbers mentally in order to estimate, and sometimes to solve for the exact answer. In the problem above, 623 + 249, many third graders should be able to mentally add 600 + 200 to get 800, and then add on 20 to get 820 and then 40 to get 860. Help students jot down intermediate results to keep track of their computation.

As students break numbers apart to add or subtract throughout the unit, make sure they continue to focus on the meaning of the quantities that these numbers represent, even as they become more practiced in carrying out multidigit computation.

Fluency in computation requires breaking numbers apart in convenient ways. In turn, breaking numbers apart requires understanding of the place-value structure of our base-ten number system. Students worked extensively in previous units with how numbers are built from 10s, 100s, and 1,000s. In this unit, they continue to focus on the meaning of the place value of the digits in the numbers they are using, for example, by using the paper clip context in Investigation 1. In *Capture from 300 to 600,* they add and subtract multiples of 10 and 100 and think through the effect of these actions on quantities.

By the end of this unit, third graders should be easily adding any 3-digit numbers with at least one strategy they can use accurately and efficiently, usually adding by place or adding number in parts to the other. Many third graders can understand and use more than one addition strategy, and

with some problems they may change the numbers in the problem to create an easier problem. See **Teacher Note:** Addition Strategies, page 152. In order to use these strategies, students must understand the meaning of addition and have a good mental model of what is happening in the problem. They should be able to look at the problem as a whole, think about the relationships of the numbers in the problem, and choose an approach that they can carry out easily and accurately. This understanding and ability grows as students solve addition problems in this unit and use number lines and 100 grids to represent their solutions.

Subtraction is, for most students, a harder operation to master fully. For subtraction, talking about the magnitude of the numbers in the problem, estimating how many 100s will be in the difference, and visualizing what is happening in each step of the solution, are all critical.

Visualizing what is happening in a variety of subtraction situations is an important foundation for understanding the operation and making good decisions about strategies for computation. Students use visual representations (such as number lines) and story contexts to help them build this understanding.

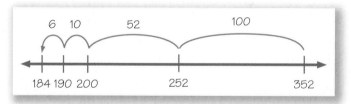

Students encounter several types of subtraction situations —removal (or "take away"), comparison, and missing parts. See **Teacher Note:** Types of Subtraction Situations, page 160. Students particularly focus on comparison problems in the context of *Collections Compare,* missing part problems in the context of distances traveled on the Oregon Trail, and removal problems in the context of earning and spending money.

By the end of this unit, students should have one subtraction method they understand and can use competently, and they should have a good grasp of the situations in which subtraction is applied. Many students will use a method in which they subtract numbers in parts. See **Teacher Note: Subtraction Strategies, page 163.** Students should also be fluent with the subtraction facts (problems related to the addition combinations to $10 + 10$) on which they are assessed early in this unit.

A key role for the teacher in this final Grade 3 unit on addition and subtraction is to work with students to refine their computation strategies and to use clear notation. For example, if some students understand a method but carry it out slowly, inefficiently, or inaccurately, what is getting in the way? Do they know their addition facts? Can they easily add (or subtract) multiples of 10? Can they keep track of parts of the numbers in the problem? Do they have a clear way to notate their steps? Can they first estimate the answer? (Some students will be able to carry out some steps mentally with ease and keep track of their process; others may still need help developing clear notation.)

Students apply their computation to many different kinds of situations in this unit, including problems with more than 2 addends, multistep problems that require both addition and subtraction, and problems in the contexts of money and distance traveled. These problems give students further opportunity to think about the meaning of and relationship between the operations of addition and subtraction.

Note that students are also assessed on their multiplication combinations (facts) in this unit (Session 1.4).

2 Whole-Number Operations Describing, analyzing, and comparing strategies for adding and subtracting whole numbers

Math Focus Points

◆ Using story contexts and representations to support explanations about how changing a number in a subtraction problem affects the difference (e.g., $200 - 75 = 125$ and $200 - 78 = 122$)

◆ Solving addition problems by changing the numbers to create an equivalent problem that is easier to solve

◆ Using story contexts and representations to support explanations about equivalent addition expressions (e.g., $88 + 105 = 90 + 103$)

◆ Identifying addition strategies by focusing on how each strategy starts

◆ Solving subtraction problems that involve comparison, removal, or finding a missing part

◆ Subtracting 3-digit numbers by using strategies that involve either subtracting one number in parts, adding up, or subtracting back

◆ Representing solutions to subtraction problems with number lines, 1,000 charts, and/or story contexts

◆ Subtracting by using strategies that involve changing one number to make a problem that is easier to solve

As students study the operations in Grades 1 through 3, they increase their understanding of the operations—their characteristics, their relationships to each other, and ways to visualize how they behave. The strategies that students use to solve computation problems are all based on characteristics of the operations. For example, they have noticed since the primary grades that when they add quantities the order of addends can be rearranged without affecting the sum. This idea of adding in any order comes up again in this unit when students work with more than two addends (see Sessions 2.4 and 2.5). Students also use the knowledge that addition and subtraction are related operations. They may add up to solve some subtraction problems, for example, thinking of $543 - 175 = ?$ as $175 + ? = 543$.

In this unit, students study two key ideas that underlie strategies for adding and subtracting. The first idea involves equivalent problems in addition. What is the sum of $1.45 and $0.96? There are many ways to solve this problem. However, since $0.96 is so close to $1.00, many of us might think of changing this problem to $1.41 + $1.00, which is an easier problem to solve mentally. Students sometimes think of this way of solving the problem as "taking 4 cents from $1.45 and giving it to the $0.96." Others think of it as "adding and subtracting the same amount." Students discuss and represent the generalization underlying this solution in Investigation 2. This work is part of the foundations of early algebra in this unit. In later years, students will learn to express this idea in symbolic notation: $a + b = (a - n) + (b + n)$.

The second key idea that students study involves subtraction. What happens to the difference when one number in a subtraction expression is changed? For example, what is the relationship between the solutions in each of these pairs of problems:

$126 - 65 = ?$	$300 - 75 = ?$
$226 - 65 = ?$	$300 - 175 = ?$

$115 - 85 = ?$	$145 - 96 = ?$
$215 - 185 = ?$	$145 - 100 = ?$

Studying such pairs of problems helps students increase their grasp of the operation of subtraction and the relationship between the numbers in a subtraction expression. This relationship is more difficult to understand than the relationship between numbers in an addition problem. Students represent, describe, and analyze these situations as part of their study of the operation of subtraction. See more about these ideas in Algebra Connections in This Unit, page 16, and in the **Teacher Note:** Reasoning and Proof in Mathematics, page 168.

This Unit also focuses on

◆ Reading and writing numbers in the thousands

◆ Fluently solving multiplication combinations with products to 50

Ten-Minute Math activities focus on

◆ Finding the multiples of numbers through skip counting

◆ Becoming familiar with multiplication patterns

◆ Understanding the relationship between skip counting and multiplication

◆ Using evidence and formulating questions to make hypotheses about the common characteristics of groups of people or things

◆ Systematically eliminating possibilities

◆ Using fractions to describe the group

LOOKING FORWARD Students should leave Grade 3 with at least one strategy for addition and one strategy for subtraction of multidigit numbers, strategies that they can use efficiently and accurately. In Grades 4 and 5, students continue to practice both operations with large numbers and to expand their repertoire of strategies. As part of a study of different procedures for each operation, they compare and analyze different strategies and algorithms, including the traditional carrying algorithm (in Grade 4) and borrowing algorithm (in Grade 5). They continue to represent and discuss generalizations about the operations that underlie their computation strategies.

Technology Note

Using The *LogoPaths* Software Students were formally introduced to the *LogoPaths* software in the 2-D Geometry and Measurement unit, *Perimeter, Angles, and Area,* the fourth unit in the Grade 3 sequence. We recommend that students continue to have access to the software **outside of math time** in order to return to *Feed the Turtle,* a *LogoPaths* activity, and to spend time with the *Free Explore* option. For information about the *LogoPaths* software and directions for *Feed the Turtle,* refer to the *Software Support Reference Guide* found on the CD. See **Part 5: Technology in *Investigations*** in *Implementing Investigations in Grade 3:* Introducing and Managing the *LogoPaths* Software in Grade 3.

Assessment

IN THIS UNIT

ONGOING ASSESSMENT: Observing Students at Work

The following sessions provide **Ongoing Assessment: Observing Students at Work** opportunities:

- **Session 1.1, pp. 30 and 34**
- **Session 1.2, p. 39**
- **Session 1.3, pp. 44–45**
- **Session 1.4, pp. 53 and 54**
- **Session 1.5, p. 59**
- **Session 2.1, p. 68**

- **Session 2.2, p. 76**
- **Session 2.3, p. 80**
- **Session 2.4, pp. 87, 88, and 90**
- **Session 3.1, p. 105**
- **Session 3.2, p. 111**

- **Session 3.3, pp. 117 and 122**
- **Session 3.4, pp. 126 and 127**
- **Session 3.6, p. 133**
- **Session 3.7, pp. 139 and 140**
- **Session 3.9, p. 147**

WRITING OPPORTUNITIES

The following sessions have **writing** opportunities for students to explain their mathematical thinking:

- **Session 1.3, p. 44**
  Student Activity Book, p. 11

- **Session 2.5, p. 95**
  Student Activity Book, p. 37

- **Session 3.3, p. 117**
  Student Activity Book, p. 45

- **Session 3.4, p. 127**
  Student Activity Book, p. 52

- **Session 3.7, p. 139**
  Student Activity Book, p. 61

- **Session 3.7, p. 141**
  Student Activity Book, pp. 65 and 66

- **Session 3.9, p. 147**
  M54, End-of-Unit Assessment

PORTFOLIO OPPORTUNITIES

The following sessions have work appropriate for a **portfolio:**

- **Session 1.4, p. 53**
  M21, Assessment: Multiplication
  Combinations

- **Session 1.5, p. 58**
  M23, Assessment: Problems About
  Capture from 300 to 600

- **Session 2.5, p. 94**
  M40, Assessment: Addition Strategies

- **Session 3.3, p. 121**
  M52, Assessment: Subtraction
  Strategies

- **Session 3.4, p. 126**
  M53, Assessment: Subtraction Facts

- **Session 3.9, p. 147**
  M54–M55, End-of-Unit Assessment

Assessing the Benchmarks

Observing students as they engage in conversation about their ideas is a primary means to assess their mathematical understanding. Consider all of your students' work, not just the written assessments. See the chart below for suggestions about key activities to observe.

See the **Differentiation and Intervention Guide** for quizzes that can be used after each Investigation.

Benchmarks in This Unit	Key Activities to Observe	Assessment
1. Add multiples of 10 and 100 (up to 1,000) to and subtract them from any 3-digit number.	**Session 1.2:** *Capture from 300 to 600*	**Session 1.5: Assessment:** Problems About *Capture from 300 to 600* ✓
2. Solve 3-digit addition problems using at least one strategy efficiently.	**Session 2.2:** Addition Starter Problems	**Session 2.5: Assessment:** Addition Strategies **Session 3.9 End-of-Unit Assessment:** Problem 1
3. Demonstrate fluency with subtraction problems related to the addition combinations to 10 + 10 (the subtraction facts).	**Sessions 3.2 and 3.3:** Homework	**Sessions 3.4 and 3.5: Assessment:** Subtraction Facts
4. Solve subtraction problems with 3-digit numbers using strategies that involve either subtracting a number in parts, adding up, or subtracting back.	**Session 3.3:** Solving a Subtraction Problem	**Session 3.3: Assessment:** Subtraction Strategies, Problem 2 **Session 3.9 End-of-Unit Assessment:** Problems 2 and 3
5. Demonstrate fluency with multiplication combinations with products up to 50.	**Session 1.2:** Homework	**Session 1.4: Assessment:** Multiplication Combinations Check

 Checklist Available

Relating the Mathematical Emphases to the Benchmarks

Mathematical Emphases	Benchmarks
Computational Fluency Adding and subtracting accurately and efficiently	1, 2, 3, and 4
Whole Number Operations Describing, analyzing, and comparing strategies for adding and subtracting whole numbers	2 and 4
Computational Fluency Fluency with multiplication combinations with products to 50	5

Algebra Connections

In this unit, your students will have opportunities to engage with ideas that lay a foundation for algebra. Eight- and 9-year-olds can and do think algebraically. Part of the work of Grade 3 is helping students learn to verbalize those thoughts and begin considering such questions as these: Is this statement *always* true? Does it work for *all* numbers? How can we know? Such discussions allow students to engage with generalizations about number and operations and also provide a foundation for meaningful use of algebraic notation in the future.

Related Problems in Subtraction

Consider the work of these students as they work with pairs of related subtraction problems from this unit.

$$126 - 65 = ?$$

$$226 - 65 = ?$$

Becky: First I found out $126 - 65 = 61$. Then I knew $226 - 65$ was 161.

$$300 - 75 = ?$$

$$300 - 175 = ?$$

Edwin: Since I knew $300 - 75$ was 225, I figured $300 - 175$ would be 125.

$$215 - 185 = ?$$

$$115 - 85 = ?$$

Kathryn: To do $215 - 185$, I just changed it to $115 - 85$. That is 30.

In each case, the students use the answer to one problem to reason about the answer to the second. Implicit in each student's work is a generalization.

First consider this vignette in which Becky and her classmates discuss her approach.

Becky: Once I knew the first one was 61, I knew the second one was 161.

Nicholas: I did that too.

Teacher: We'd like to hear more. Tell us how you were thinking about these.

Becky: I used the paper clip boxes. In the second problem there is an extra box of paper clips, so it will be 100 more at the end.

Nicholas: What I did was different. I drew a number line. For the first one, you go from 65 to 126. For the second one you have to do that and then you have to go another 100. If the first one is 61, the second is 161.

In this vignette, students are combining their knowledge of the place-value system and their understanding of the operation of subtraction to reason about a computation problem. Underlying their work is a generalization about subtraction: If you subtract the same amount from a quantity that has been increased by 100, the difference will be 100 greater. This idea can be expressed like this: If $a - b = c$ then $(a + 100) - b = (c + 100)$. In this example, the students are focused on adding 100 because they are also working on ideas of place value; however, this principle is true for any number, not just 100. For instance, when students use the answer to $500 - 93$ to reason about the answer to $520 - 93$, they are also calling upon this principle. In later years this idea will be expressed as: If $a - b = c$, then $(a + n) - b = (c + n)$.

Now, consider this conversation about Edwin's approach to $300 - 75$ and $300 - 175$.

Edwin: I thought about the paper clip boxes. In the second problem you have to take away an extra box, so the answer will be 100 fewer than the first.

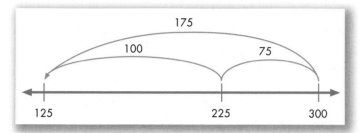

Zhang: I thought about moving on the number line. You start at 300 for both, but in the first one you go back 75 and land on 225. For the second one, you still have to go back another 100 after that. The answer to the second one has to be 100 less, so that's 125.

Bridget: I thought about money. If my brother and I both have $3.00 and I spend a dollar more than he does, then I will have a dollar less. $3.00 − $0.75 is what my brother has, $2.25. $3.00 − $1.75 is what I have, only $1.25.

In this brief vignette, Edwin reasons with the paper clip context, Zhang uses a number line, and Bridget uses money as a context. All are calling upon a general principle about subtraction: If you subtract more, you end up with less. In later years, this idea could be expressed as: If $a - b = c$, then $a - (b + n) = c - n$.

Next, consider this discussion in which Kathryn and her classmates explain their thinking about $215 - 185$ and $115 - 85$.

Kathryn: I figured if the first one was 30, then the second one was 30 too. I thought about the paper clip boxes. If you take away one box, then you have 115 left, and you still have to take away the 85. So it's the same as the first problem. That doesn't change the answer.

Arthur: I pictured it on a number line. For the first one I started at 85 and moved 15 to 100 and then another 15 to 115. Then I started the second problem by moving from 185 to 200 and then to 215. It is just doing the same thing again. I bet $315 - 285$ would be the same. It is 15 on one side of a hundreds number and 15 on the other side of the hundreds number, so it's 30. Any problem like that is the same.

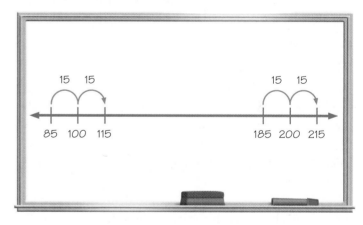

Teacher: Arthur is saying that $115 - 85$, $215 - 185$, $315 - 285$ all have the same answer. Kathryn is using the paper clip boxes to think about this, and Arthur is picturing a number line. Let's look at this some more. What is happening with these problems? Can someone say what he or she sees?

Bridget: The numbers stay the same apart.

Kenji: You are adding 100 to both of them.

Teacher: Do you think that will *always* happen? If you add 100 to both numbers in a subtraction problem, will the answer be the same? Bridget is talking about the numbers staying the same amount apart. How does that help you to think about this question? You might want to use number lines, paper clip boxes, story contexts, diagrams, or other kinds of math tools we have been using. Can you show this will always be true? Not just for these numbers, but for other subtraction problems as well?

This vignette illustrates an important relationship in subtraction problems: If $a - b = c$, then $(a + 100) - (b + 100) = c$. In fact, this is a specific example of a more general principle of subtraction: If you add (or subtract) the same quantity to or from both of the numbers in a subtraction problem, the difference remains the same. In later years this principle might be expressed as $(a + n) - (b + n) = a - b$ or $(a - n) - (b - n) = a - b$. In *How Many Hundreds? How Many Miles?*, students call upon this property to change a subtraction problem into one that is easier to solve. For example, one way to solve $145 - 96$ is to add 4 to each quantity, resulting in an easier problem with the same difference, $149 - 100$.

Let us return to the vignette to see how the class responded to the teacher's challenge to explain.

Gina: I used the paper clip boxes. There are two people with some paper clips. One has more than the other. If I give them both a box with 100 clips, it won't matter. The person with more will still have that same amount more.

Philip: I thought about money. If I have more money than my brother and we each get a dollar, I still have the same amount more than he does.

Keith: I made a drawing like this. One is more than the other, so it is longer.

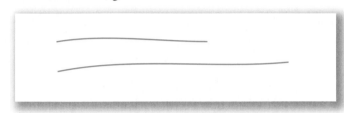

If I add the same amount to both, the one that is longer stays the same amount longer.

In this vignette, Gina uses the paper clip context, Philip uses a story context based on money, and Keith makes a drawing to explain why adding 100 to each number in a subtraction problem does not change the difference. Keith's diagrams and the arguments offered by Gina and Philip could also support a more general statement about adding any number to both quantities in a subtraction problem.

When such representations are shared, students should be encouraged to explain the connections among the diagram, the story context, and the arithmetic expressions to help them articulate their reasoning. How does Keith's drawing match Gina's story about the paper clips or Philip's story about money? How does the drawing show adding 100? Is there a way to use Keith's drawing (or Gina's paper clips or Philip's story) to see what happens if you add numbers other than 100?

Investigations students are encouraged to verbalize the generalizations they see about numbers and operations, and to explain and justify them using materials and tools, such as story contexts or diagrams. For most adults, notation such as the use of variables, operations, and equal signs is the chief identifying feature of algebra. Underlying such notation, however, are ways of reasoning about how the operations work. This *reasoning*—about how numbers can be put together and taken apart under different operations—not the notation, is the work of elementary students in algebra.

Note: In the text for the sessions, you will find Algebra Notes that identify where these early algebra discussions are likely to arise. Some of the **Teacher Notes** and **Dialogue Boxes** further elaborate the ideas and illustrate students' conversations about them.

Classroom Routines and Ten-Minute Math

IN THIS UNIT

The **Classroom Routines** and **Ten-Minute Math** activities, to be done in ten minutes outside of math class, are introduced in a unit and repeated throughout the grade. Specific directions for the day's activity are provided in each session. For the full description and variations of the Classroom Routines and Ten-Minute Math activities, see *Implementing Investigations in Grade 3*.

Activity	Introduced	Full Description of Activity and Its Variations
Classroom Routines: *What's the Temperature?*	Unit 1, Session 1.1	*Implementing Investigations in Grade 3*
Ten-Minute Math: *Guess My Rule*	Unit 2, Session 1.3	*Implementing Investigations in Grade 3*
Ten-Minute Math: *Counting Around the Class*	Unit 5, Session 1.3	*Implementing Investigations in Grade 3*

What's the Temperature?

Students record the outside temperature every Wednesday morning on a chart and on a graph. They continue to practice reading charts and graphs, considering the relationship between them, and discussing changes in temperature over time.

Guess My Rule

Students decide, through careful observation and questioning, a "rule" that the leader established. The leader identifies specific people or items that do and do not fit the rule to get the game started. Students use this evidence to make guesses in order to deduce the rule. They also discuss what fraction fits the rule.

Math Focus Points

◆ Using evidence and formulating questions to make hypotheses about the common characteristics of groups of people or things

◆ Systematically eliminating possibilities

◆ Using fractions to describe the group

Counting Around the Class

Students count around the class by a particular number. Before the count starts, they estimate the ending number of the count and the number the last person in the class will say. Students discuss relationships between the chosen factor and its multiples.

Math Focus Points

◆ Finding the multiples of numbers through skip counting

◆ Becoming familiar with multiplication patterns

◆ Understanding the relationship between skip counting and multiplication

Practice and Review

Practice and review play a critical role in the *Investigations* program. The following components and features are available to provide regular reinforcement of key mathematical concepts and procedures.

Books	Features	In This Unit ...
Curriculum Unit	**The Classroom Routines** and **Ten-Minute Math** activities, to be done in ten minutes outside of math class, are introduced in a unit and repeated throughout the grade. Specific directions for the day's activity are provided in each session. For the full description and variations of the Classroom Routines and Ten-Minute Math activities, see *Implementing Investigations in Grade 3*.	• **All sessions**
Student Activity Book	**Daily Practice** pages in the *Student Activity Book* provide one of three types of written practice: **reinforcement** of the content of the unit, **ongoing review,** or **enrichment** opportunities. Some Daily Practice pages will also have Ongoing Review items with multiple-choice problems similar to those on standardized tests.	• **All sessions**
	Homework pages in the *Student Activity Book* are an extension of the work done in class. At times they help students prepare for upcoming activities.	• **Session 1.2** • **Session 3.1** • **Session 1.3** • **Session 3.2** • **Session 1.5** • **Session 3.3** • **Session 2.2** • **Session 3.4** • **Session 2.4** • **Session 3.6** • **Session 3.7**
Student Math Handbook	**Math Words and Ideas** in the *Student Math Handbook* are pages that summarize key words and ideas. Most Words and Ideas pages have at least one exercise.	• **Student Math Handbook, pp. 10–12, 16–38, 40–41, 47–49, 56, 58–60, 64**
	Games pages are found in a section of the *Student Math Handbook*.	• **Student Math Handbook, pp. G1, G2, G8, G9**

Differentiation

Supporting the Range of Learners

The **Differentiation and Intervention Guide** provides Intervention, Extension, and Practice activities for use within each Investigation.

Sessions	1.1	1.3	1.4	1.5	2.1	2.2	2.3	2.4	3.1	3.2	3.3	3.5	3.6	3.7	3.9
Intervention	•		•	•	•	•	•	•	•	•	•			•	•
Extension		•				•		•		•			•		
ELL	•						•			•		•			

Intervention

Suggestions are made to support and engage students who are having difficulty with a particular idea, activity, or problem.

Extension

Suggestions are made to support and engage students who finish early or may be ready for additional challenge.

English Language Learners (ELL)

As English Language Learners work through the activities and games in *How Many Hundreds? How Many Miles?*, the computational fluency they have developed in earlier units will support them in using numbers to explain how they solved a problem, both in their written work and in whole-class discussions.

To develop their language skills for orally explaining their solution methods, offer extra support in the use of past tense verbs, both regular and irregular. Make a list of verbs that are likely to come up during class discussions of students' strategies in this unit. For example:

added	made	subtracted	traveled
broke apart	put	sorted	went
changed	solved		

Write each verb in a short, math-related sentence at the top of a piece of paper and ask students to illustrate the sentences, using numerical notation when appropriate.

For example: "I **broke apart** 623 into hundreds, tens, and ones." Students could write in the space below:
$$623 = 600 + 20 + 3$$

Collect these sheets in a binder. Read this "verb book" aloud while English Language Learners repeat each sentence after you. Remind students that some verbs add –*ed* at the end to show the past tense, while others change their form. Emphasize the verbs that change form. Keep the book out during math lessons for use as a reference.

You can make sure that English Language Learners understand written and oral directions by asking them to paraphrase the information. Minimize as much as possible the number of directions you give at one time. Stop after each direction and ask students to repeat it in their own words. Supply words as necessary.

Working with the Range of Learners: Classroom Cases is a set of episodes written by teachers that focuses on meeting the needs of the range of learners in the classroom. In the first section, *Setting up the Mathematical Community,* teachers write about how they create a supportive and productive learning environment in their classrooms. In the next section, *Accommodations for Learning,* teachers focus on specific modifications they make to meet the needs of some of their learners. In the last section, *Language and Representation,* teachers share how they help students use representations and develop language to investigate and express mathematical ideas. The questions at the end of each case provide a starting point for your own reflection or for discussion with colleagues. See *Implementing Investigations in Grade 3* for this set of episodes.

Mathematical Emphases

Computational Fluency Adding and subtracting accurately and efficiently

Math Focus Points

◆ Combining hundreds to numbers above 1,000

◆ Subtracting from multiples of 100

◆ Adding multiples of 10 and 100 to, and subtracting them from, 3-digit numbers

◆ Estimating answers to subtraction problems with 3-digit numbers

◆ Using the relationship of numbers in a subtraction expression to multiples of 100 to solve subtraction problems

Whole-Number Operations Describing, analyzing, and comparing strategies for adding and subtracting whole numbers

Math Focus Points

◆ Using story contexts and representations to support explanations about how changing a number in a subtraction problem affects the difference (e.g., $200 - 75 = 125$ and $200 - 78 = 122$)

This Investigation also focuses on

◆ Reading and writing numbers in the thousands
◆ Fluently solving multiplication combinations with products to 50

Numbers in the Hundreds

	Student Activity Book	Student Math Handbook	Professional Development: Read Ahead of Time	
SESSION 1.1　　　　p. 28				
Paper Clip Problems　Students combine hundreds to numbers above 1,000 and solve problems in which they subtract 2- and 3-digit numbers from multiples of 100.	1–5	32–35	• **Part 4: Ten-Minute Math and Classroom Routines** in *Implementing Investigations in Grade 3:* Counting Around the Class • **Mathematics in This Unit,** p. 10 • **Part 4: Ten-Minute Math and Classroom Routines** in *Implementing Investigations in Grade 3:* What's the Temperature?	
SESSION 1.2　　　　p. 36				
Capture from 300 to 600　Students play a variation of the game *Capture 5,* in which ones, tens, and hundreds are added to and subtracted from 3-digit numbers between 300 and 600. They continue to solve problems involving adding to and subtracting from multiples of 100.	2–4, 6–9	G1–G2		
SESSION 1.3　　　　p. 40				
Related Subtraction Problems　Students practice estimation strategies by focusing on how many hundreds there are in answers to subtraction problems. They solve sets of related problems that involve subtracting from multiples of 100 and numbers near multiples of 100.	11–13	32–35; G1–G2		

Classroom Routines and Ten-Minute Math

See page 20 for an overview.

What's the Temperature?

- Mount the thermometer outside the classroom window.
- Post the Date and Temperature chart and Temperature graph in the classroom.

Counting Around the Class

- No materials needed

Materials to Gather | Materials to Prepare

- **Boxes of 100 paper clips** (1 per student; optional). Alternatively, use 100 grids; see Materials to Prepare.

- **M1–M6,** *LogoPaths: Missing Measures and Steps* Make copies for ongoing use of the computer with the *LogoPaths* software. (1 per student; optional)
- **M9, 100 Grids** Make copies. (1 sheet per student; plus 1 cut-apart grid per student, if needed as alternative to boxes of paper clips)
- **M7–M8, Family Letter** Make copies. (1 per student)

- **T94–T96, 301–600 Chart**
- **T97–T98, Plus/Minus Cards**
- **T99,** *Capture from 300 to 600* **Recording Sheet**
- **Plus/Minus Cards** (from Unit 3; 1 set per pair)
- **Colored chips** (30 per pair or group)
- **Centimeter cubes** (1 per student or 2 per group)
- **Scissors** (as needed)
- **Tape or glue sticks**
- **Multiplication Cards** (from Unit 5, if available; 1 set per student)

- **M10–M11,** *Capture from 300 to 600* Play a few rounds ahead of time to familiarize yourself with the mathematics involved in this game.
- **M12–M14, 301–600 Chart** Make copies. (1 set for each student)
- **M15–M16, Plus/Minus Cards** Make copies and cut apart to replace lost cards. (1 set per pair; as needed)
- **M17,** *Capture from 300 to 600* **Recording Sheet** Make copies. (as needed)
- **M18, Blank Multiplication Cards** Make copies. (1 per student)

- **M12–M14, 301–600 Chart** (1 per pair or group; from Session 1.2)
- **M15–M16, Plus/Minus Cards** (1 set per pair or group; from Unit 3 or Session 1.2)
- **Colored chips** (30 per pair or group)
- **Centimeter cubes** (1 per student or 2 per group)

- **Chart paper** Write the following problem on chart paper: *Elena has 5 boxes of paper clips. She uses 38 paper clips. How many paper clips are left?*
- **M17,** *Capture from 300 to 600* **Recording Sheet** Make copies. (as needed)
- **M19–M20, Family Letter** Make copies. (1 per student)

Overhead Transparency

Numbers in the Hundreds,
continued

	Student Activity Book	Student Math Handbook	Professional Development: Read Ahead of Time	
SESSION 1.4 p. 47				
Assessment: Multiplication Combinations Students discuss the ways in which increasing or decreasing the numbers in a subtraction problem affects the answer. They practice solving subtraction problems and are assessed on their knowledge of multiplication combinations with products to 50.	11, 15–17	32–35, 49–51	• **Dialogue Box:** I Know It's Either 2 More or 2 Less, p. 176 • **Teacher Note:** Learning and Assessing Multiplication Combinations, p. 149	
SESSION 1.5 p. 55				
Assessment: Operations with Multiples of 10 and 100 Students discuss and represent the relationship between two subtraction problems that differ by multiples of 100. They are assessed on their fluency with adding and subtracting multiples of 10 and 100. An assessment checklist is provided.	15–16, 18–19	32–35; G1–G2		

Materials to Gather	Materials to Prepare
	• **Chart paper** Write the problem shown on page 48 on chart paper: • **M9, 100 Grids** Make copies. (1 per student) • **M21, Assessment: Multiplication Combinations** Make copies. (1 per student) • **M22, Blank Multiplication Combinations** Make copies. (as needed)
	• **M9, 100 Grids** Make copies. (as needed) • **Chart paper** Write the two problems found on page 56 on chart paper. • **M23, Assessment: Problems About *Capture from 300 to 600*** Make copies. (1 per student) • **M24, Assessment Checklist: Adding and Subtracting Multiples of 10 and 100** ☑ Make copies. (as needed for your class)

☑ Checklist Available

Paper Clip Problems

Math Focus Points

◆ Combining hundreds to numbers above 1,000

◆ Subtracting from multiples of 100

◆ Reading and writing numbers in the thousands

Today's Plan		Materials
ACTIVITY **①** *Counting Around the Class* 10 MIN CLASS		
ACTIVITY **②** **Introducing Paper Clip Problems** 20 MIN PAIRS CLASS		• *Student Activity Book,* p. 1 • M9* • Boxes of 100 paper clips
ACTIVITY **③** **Paper Clip Problems** 30 MIN PAIRS		• *Student Activity Book,* pp. 2–4 • M9 (as needed) • Boxes of 100 paper clips
SESSION FOLLOW-UP **④** **Daily Practice**		• *Student Activity Book,* p. 5 • *Student Math Handbook,* pp. 32–35 • M7–M8, Family Letter*

*See *Materials to Prepare,* p. 25.

Ten-Minute Math

Counting Around the Class Students count around the class by 5s. Each student says another multiple of 5 until all students have counted once. Highlight the multiples of 5 by writing them on the board as students say them. Ask how many students have counted at 25, 50, and 100.

ACTIVITY

1 Counting Around the Class

10 MIN   CLASS

Begin this session by reminding students of the Ten-Minute Math activity, *Counting Around the Class,* which they last did during the unit *Equal Groups.*

Today we are going to count around the class by 100. What number will the 10th person say? How do you know?

To answer this question, students should be able to call upon their previous work in the Grade 3 unit, *Collections and Travel Stories,* building 1,000 from groups of 100.

Ask three or four students whose predictions are close to the correct number to explain how they made their predictions.

Students might say:

"I know that there are 10 hundreds in 1 thousand, so 1,000 is the number the tenth person will say."

If we count by 100 and everyone says one number, what number do you think the last person will say? You don't need to figure out the exact number, just an estimate of about what the number will be. ❶

Collect enough responses to get a sense of what students understand about the structure of numbers above 1,000. For example, if your class contains around 20 students, listen to hear whether students build on knowledge of 10 hundreds in 1,000 to make predictions close to 2,000. Are there students who make predictions that are not reasonable estimates? Since students have not yet worked with numbers this large, do not expect them all to be able to reason about multiples of 100 and 1,000. This activity and the one to follow will help students make that connection.

Ask several students whose predictions are close to the correct number to explain how they made their predictions.

Students might say:

"I predicted the number would be around 2,000 because I know that the 10th person will say 1,000 and I think there are about 20 of us here today. Since 20 is double 10, the answer has to be double 1,000. That's 2,000."

"I predicted 2,400. I know that 10 hundreds make 1,000, and 10 more hundreds would be another 1,000. That's 2,000 in all. I think that there are a few more than 20 students here, so that's why I said 2,400."

Now count around the class by 100. As students count, some may be unsure about how to name and write numbers greater than 1,000. For example, the eleventh person might say "11 hundred." If this happens, write 1,100 on the board and say something like the following:

Sometimes we do say "11 hundred" for this number, and that makes sense since it does contain 11 hundreds. What's another name we use for this number?

As students continue, stop from time to time to ask students how to write the number just counted and how they would read it. Students may be confused by the fact that there are two acceptable ways to name multiples of 100 above 1,000. For example, the number 1,700 can be read as both "17 hundred" "and "1 thousand, 7 hundred." Ask students why they think this is true. Some may be able to articulate that 1,700 is composed of 17 hundreds, but is also composed of 1 thousand and 7 hundreds. Do not spend a lot of time on this because students will develop this idea as they work through this Investigation.

ONGOING ASSESSMENT: Observing Students at Work

Students count by 100.

- **Can students say the next multiple of 100?** Do they know which multiple of 100 comes after 1,000? After 2,000?

- **Do students know how to say multiples of 100 that are greater than 1,000?**

ACTIVITY

2 Introducing Paper Clip Problems

20 MIN   PAIRS   CLASS

Hold up a box of paper clips. Show students where it says that there are 100 paper clips in the box. Then pass out one box to each student. As an alternative, you could distribute one 100 grid to each student, cut from copies of 100 Grids (M9). If you use the 100 grids, talk with students about how each grid represents one box of paper clips, and how each individual box in the grid therefore stands for 1 paper clip.

Ask some questions that involve combining the boxes. Name students and groups in your class to make these questions interesting. Try to use some smaller and some larger combinations. For example:

- If Becky, Adam, Deondra, and Zhang put their boxes of paper clips together, how many would they have?

- If all the students who wear glasses put their boxes together, how many paper clips would they have?

- If all the girls in the class combined their boxes, how many paper clips would they have? How many would the boys have if they put their boxes together?

- What if we put all our boxes together? How many paper clips would we have in all?

For some of these questions, students will combine hundreds to make numbers in the thousands. Encourage them to count up by 100 to get to the appropriate number and to name these numbers in two ways (e.g., both 2 thousand 1 hundred and 21 hundred).

To prepare students for their work in the *Student Activity Book,* hold up two boxes of 100 paper clips and present the following problem:

We know that there are 100 paper clips in each box. Imagine that I need to use 12 paper clips to put together some papers for a meeting I have tonight. [Take 12 paper clips out of one of the boxes.] With a partner, figure out how many paper clips I have left.

Give students time to work on this problem in pairs. You might suggest that students use number lines or the 100 grids on *Student Activity Book* page 1 to model and represent the problem.

Bring the class back together to discuss how students solved the problem.

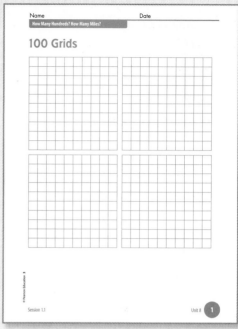

▲ **Student Activity Book, p. 1; M9**

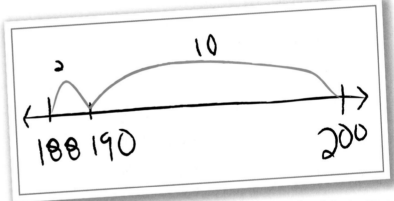

Student Activity Book, p. 2

Paper Clip Problems (page 1 of 3)

Solve these problems. Show your solutions.
Remember, each box contains 100 paper clips.

1. Mrs. Lopez had 3 boxes of paper clips. How many paper clips did she have? She gave 20 clips to another teacher. How many clips does she have left?

2. **a.** Joel and his cousin bought 4 boxes of paper clips. How many paper clips did they have?

   b. They used 45 paper clips for a school project. How many paper clips do they have now?

2   Unit 8   Sessions 1.1, 1.2

Students might say:

"We subtracted 12 from 100—that's 88—and then we put the other hundred back, because it's really 200 minus 12. So it's 188."

"We started at 200 and subtracted 10 to 190 and 2 more to 188, so you have 188 paper clips left."

"We knew that 12 + 88 = 100, so if you take 12 out of one box you have 88 left. You didn't take any paper clips out of the other box so it still has 100. That means that you have 188 paper clips left."

Ask students who used either a number line or the 100 grids to share their representations. Subtracting 10 and then 2 is a useful strategy for this problem. If no one has already made a number line representation of this strategy, ask a volunteer to do so.

Sample Student Work

The 100 grids provide a visual representation of how 200 − 12 can be related to an easier problem, 100 − 12. Students can see that the 12 came out of only one box of 100, leaving the second box intact.

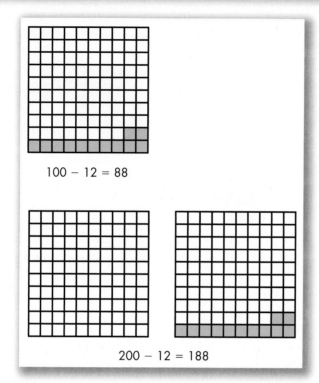

$$100 - 12 = 88$$

$$200 - 12 = 188$$

Students will continue to work on using what they know about subtracting from 100 to subtract from multiples of 100 as they solve the paper clip problems and others in this and the next few sessions.

Help students reflect on their strategies by saying something like the following:

Some of you solved these problems by subtracting 10 and then 2 from either 100 or 200. Others knew the combination to make 100, 12 + 88, and knew that if 12 + 88 equals 100, then 100 − 12 equals 88 and 200 − 12 equals 188. Let's keep these strategies in mind as you solve some more problems about paper clips.

ACTIVITY
③ Paper Clip Problems

30 MIN **PAIRS**

Students work in pairs on *Student Activity Book* pages 2–4. Even though they work together on the solutions, emphasize that it is important for each student to have a record of their work. Remind students that they may use 100 grids or number lines to help them visualize what is happening in the problems. For those students who have used up the grids on *Student Activity Book* page 1, make available copies of 100 Grids (M9).

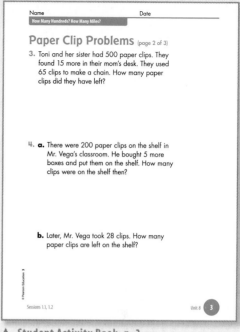

▲ Student Activity Book, p. 3

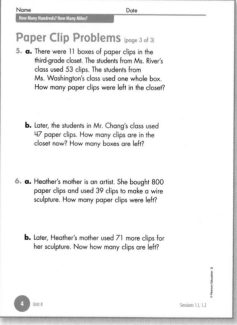

▲ Student Activity Book, p. 4

*Paper clip problems help students practice subtracting
from multiples of 100.*

As students work on these paper clip problems, encourage them to
think about how using known combinations that add up to 100 can
help them solve these problems. Also remind them that knowing the
difference between 100 and a number less than 100 can help them
figure out the difference between a multiple of 100 and the same
number (e.g., if $100 - 12 = 88$, then $200 - 12 = 188$).

Most students will not have time to finish all these problems in this
session. They will have more time in Math Workshop in the next session.

ONGOING ASSESSMENT: Observing Students at Work

Students solve problems that involve combining and then subtracting
from groups of 100s.

- **What strategies do students use for subtracting?** Do they subtract
  back? Do they add up? Do they use larger chunks of numbers rather
  than counting by 1s or 10s?

- **Are students using combinations that add up to 100 to help
  them solve these problems?**

- **Do some students represent their strategies on 100 grids or
  number lines?** Do some students solve problems mentally?

DIFFERENTIATION: Supporting the Range of Learners

As you circulate, observe whether the size of the numbers is at the right level of challenge for each student. If not, you can help the student choose a problem that is more appropriate or, if need be, adapt the problems by making the numbers larger or smaller.

Intervention Some students who are having difficulty may need more help to visualize the problems. The sticker sketches they used earlier in the year may be helpful. Model for them how to draw a quick sketch of the problem they are working on. If they find it useful, they can continue this with other problems.

$$400 - 45 = 355$$

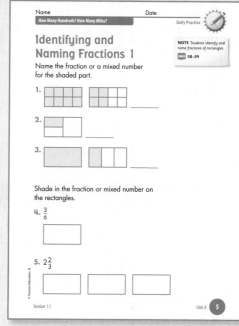

▲ **Student Activity Book, p. 5**

SESSION FOLLOW-UP

4 Daily Practice

Daily Practice: For ongoing review, have students complete *Student Activity Book* page 5.

Student Math Handbook: Students and families may use *Student Math Handbook* pages 32–35 for reference and review. See pages 179–189 in the back of this unit.

Family Letter: Send home copies of the Family Letter (M7–M8).

Capture from 300 to 600

Math Focus Points

◆ Subtracting from multiples of 100

◆ Adding multiples of 10 and 100 to, and subtracting them from, 3-digit numbers

Vocabulary

positive
negative

Today's Plan

		Materials
1 ACTIVITY **Introducing** *Capture from 300 to 600*	🕐 15 MIN 👥 CLASS	• M10–M11*; M12–M14; M15–M16; M17; T94–T96; T97–T98 🖥
2 MATH WORKSHOP **Practicing Addition and Subtraction** **2A** *Capture from 300 to 600* **2B** Paper Clip Problems	🕐 45 MIN	**2A** • *Student Activity Book,* p. 6 • M12–M14*; M15–M16*; M17 (as needed)*; T99 🖥 • Colored chips; centimeter cubes; scissors; tape or glue sticks **2B** • *Student Activity Book,* pp. 2–4 • M9 (as needed)* • Boxes of 100 paper clips
3 SESSION FOLLOW-UP **Daily Practice and Homework**		• *Student Activity Book,* pp. 6–9 • M18* • *Student Math Handbook,* pp. G1–G2

*See *Materials to Prepare,* p. 25.

Ten-Minute Math

Counting Around the Class Students count around the class by 10s. Ask students if the ending answer will be larger or smaller than when they counted by 5s. Ask for predictions for what the last number will be. Each student says another multiple of 10 until all students have counted once. Highlight the multiples of 10 by writing them on the board as students say them. Ask how many students have counted at 90, 180, and 200.

ACTIVITY

Introducing *Capture from 300 to 600*

15 MIN CLASS

The game *Capture from 300 to 600* is an extension of the game *Capture 5,* which students played in the first Grade 3 unit, *Trading Stickers, Combining Coins.* In the original game, students added and subtracted single-digit numbers and multiples of 10 in order to capture chips that had been placed on a 100 chart. In Unit 3, *Collections and Travel Stories,* students played a version of this game on a 300 chart, adding and subtracting multiples of 100 as well as multiples of 10 and single-digit numbers. In this newest version of the game, students use a gameboard with numbers from 301 to 600.

Students should be familiar enough with this game to not need a complete demonstration, as the only difference in this version is the size of the numbers. Explain that you will be handing out copies of the 301–600 Chart (M12–M14) and Plus/Minus Cards (M15–M16) when they play in Math Workshop, and they will use the recording sheet on *Student Activity Book* page 6.

Remind students that, as with the 300 chart, they will need to put together the three pages of the 301–600 chart into a single gameboard before they play the game, and cut out the Plus/Minus Cards if they have not already been cut apart. Have available *Capture from 300 to 600* (M10–M11) for a review of the game rules.

In this version of the *Capture* game, students also find how many spaces they move in all, which involves combining positive and negative changes. Introduce this part of the activity by asking students to find the difference between starting and ending numbers in an imaginary round of the game. Use the transparent gameboard 301–600 Chart (T94–T96) and Plus/Minus Cards (T97–T98) on the overhead to demonstrate this round. For example:

Let's say we started at 416 and ended at 473, and our Plus/Minus Cards were +50, +20, −10, and −3. How many spaces did we move altogether? How can you quickly count that up on the 401 − 500 chart? How can you use the Plus/Minus Cards to find the number of spaces we moved?

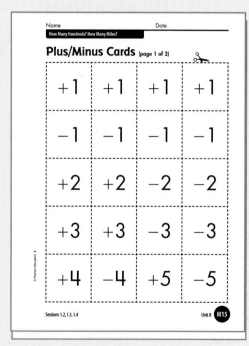

▲ Resource Masters, M12–M14; T94–T96

▲ Resource Masters, M15–M16; T97–T98

Math Notes

❶ Positive and Negative Change When students record the number of spaces they have moved in *Capture from 300 to 600,* they are actually recording the *absolute value* of their move. That is, they are calculating the difference between the starting and ending numbers without regard to the direction of the move. If their changes are $50 + 20 - 10 - 3$, they have moved a total of 57 spaces in a positive direction. If their changes are $- 50 - 20 + 10 + 3$, they have also moved 57 spaces, but in a negative direction. In this case, their ending number is less than their starting number.

❷ Combining in Any Order Some students will combine expressions in the order in which they are written—from left to right. For example, they will calculate $50 + 20 - 10 - 3$ in this way: $50 + 20 = 70, 70 - 10 = 60, 60 - 3 = 57$. Others might combine the positive and the negative changes first and then combine the results: $50 + 20 = 70$, $-10 - 3 = -13$, and then $70 - 13 = 57$. In either of these computations, adding a change of -10 or -3 is represented as subtracting 10 or subtracting 3.

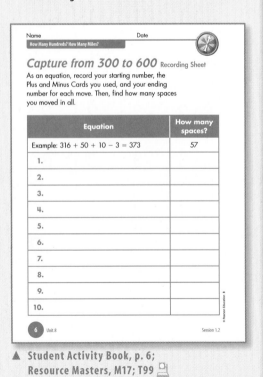

▲ Student Activity Book, p. 6;
Resource Masters, M17; T99

Give students a few minutes to work out the problem. Help students see that by combining the positive and negative changes, they come up with the same result as they do by counting on the chart; that is, $50 + 20 - 10 - 3 = 57$. Then ask them to consider whether the overall change was positive or negative. ❶ ❷

Did we end at a number that was greater or less than our starting number?

Give students another example in which the total of the negative cards is greater than the total of the positive cards.

What if we started at 416, but had these cards instead: -50, -20, $+10$, and $+3$. Will the number we end on be greater than 416, or less than 416? How do you know?

Give students a minute to talk about this with a partner, and then collect their responses.

What do you think that tells us about the amount of positive change we had in this round compared to the amount of negative change?

MATH WORKSHOP

45 MIN

❷ Practicing Addition and Subtraction

In this Math Workshop, students play the new game *Capture from 300 to 600.* They also continue working on the paper clip problems from the previous session. Students will discuss Problem 6 at the beginning of the next session.

❷A *Capture from 300 to 600*

PAIRS GROUPS

Students play the game in pairs or two teams of 2. Each pair or group will need a gameboard (the 301–600 Chart taped or glued together) and a set of Plus/Minus Cards. Provide each pair or group with colored chips and centimeter cubes to use as game pieces. Make available copies of *Capture from 300 to 600* Recording Sheet (M17) for use after students have completed the recording sheet on *Student Activity Book* page 6.

ONGOING ASSESSMENT: Observing Students at Work

Students add and subtract single-digit numbers and multiples of 10 and 100.

- **Do students mentally add and subtract multiples of 10, or do they count rows each time?**

- **Do students recognize which digits of the starting number will remain the same in the ending number (e.g., that adding or subtracting a multiple of 100 does not affect the digits in the tens and ones places)?**

2B Paper Clip Problems

PAIRS

For complete details about this activity, see Session 1.1, page 31.

SESSION FOLLOW-UP

Daily Practice and Homework

Daily Practice: For reinforcement of this unit's content, have students complete *Student Activity Book* page 7.

Homework: Have students take home *Student Activity Book* pages 8–9. They will also need a copy of Blank Multiplication Cards (M18). Students should still have at home the Multiplication Cards that they have been working with since Unit 5, *Equal Groups.* As they did earlier in the year with addition combinations, they go through their cards and write up to 6 combinations that they are still working on. They practice these combinations at home with a friend or family member and record the details of this practice on *Student Activity Book* page 9.

Alert students that you will be assessing their knowledge of the multiplication combinations with products to 50 in Session 1.4.

Student Math Handbook: Students and families may use *Student Math Handbook* pages G1 and G2 for reference and review. See pages 179–189 in the back of this unit.

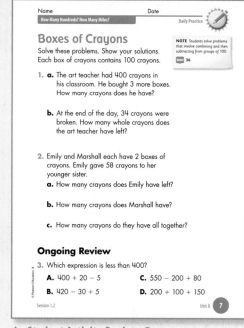

▲ Student Activity Book, p. 7

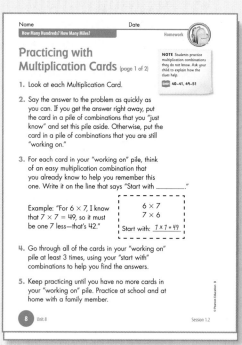

▲ Student Activity Book, pp. 8–9

Related Subtraction Problems

Math Focus Points

◆ Adding multiples of 10 and 100 to, and subtracting them from, 3-digit numbers

◆ Estimating answers to subtraction problems with 3-digit numbers

◆ Using the relationship of numbers in a subtraction expression to multiples of 100 to solve subtraction problems

Vocabulary

hundreds

Today's Plan		Materials
① DISCUSSION **Estimating Your Answer** 15 MIN · CLASS		• Chart paper with story problem*
② MATH WORKSHOP **Practicing Addition and Subtraction** **2A** Related Subtraction Problems **2B** *Capture from 300 to 600* 45 MIN		**2A** • *Student Activity Book,* p. 11 **2B** • Materials from Session 1.2, p. 36
③ SESSION FOLLOW-UP **Daily Practice and Homework**		• *Student Activity Book,* pp. 12–13 • *Student Math Handbook,* pp. 32–35; G1–G2 • M19–M20, Family Letter*

*See *Materials to Prepare,* p. 25.

Ten-Minute Math

Counting Around the Class Students count around the class by 25s. Ask students if the ending answer will be larger or smaller than when they counted by 10s. Ask for predictions for what the last number will be. (Many students will simply predict any large number they can think of.) Each student says another multiple of 25 until all students have counted once. Highlight the multiples of 25 by writing them on the board as students say them. Ask how many students have counted at 200, 325, and 400.

DISCUSSION

① Estimating Your Answer

15 MIN CLASS

Math Focus Points for Discussion

◆ Estimating answers to subtraction problems with 3-digit numbers

Call attention to the problem that you prepared on chart paper.

> Elena has 5 boxes of paper clips.
> She uses 38 paper clips.
> How many paper clips are left?

Don't try to find the exact answer to this problem yet. First, think about what you know about the answer. How many hundreds are in the answer? (400) Is the answer closer to 400 or to 500? Why do you think so?

Give students some time to offer their responses to these questions. Some students may want to use a number line or another representation to explain their answer.

Now suppose Elena starts with 5 boxes of paper clips and 50 additional ones. She uses 38 paper clips. How many hundreds are in the number she has left? Which multiple of 100 is it closer to? How do you know?

Students might say:

"There are five hundreds in the answer because if you take away 38 paper clips from the 50 extra ones, you still end up over 500."

"You're closer to 500 than 600 because the difference between 38 and 50 isn't much."

Students might offer this representation:

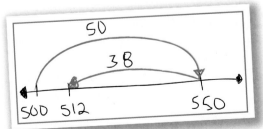

Sample Student Work

When students understand the thinking behind the idea that 550 − 38 is more than 500, pose the next problem.

Elena again starts with 550 paper clips. She uses 72 paper clips this time. How many hundreds are there in the number of paper clips she has left? Which multiple of 100 is it closer to? How do you know?

Give students a few minutes to talk with a partner about this problem, and then ask for answers.

Students might say:

"Elena uses 72 paper clips, so she must use up all the paper clips more than 500 and 22 more. So there are only 4 hundreds in what she has left."

"And she's using only 22 less than 500, so the answer is closer to 500 than to 400."

"Elena starts with 500 paper clips and five extra tens. 72 has seven 10s in it, so she uses all five extra 10s and 2 more tens. So there are four hundreds in the answer."

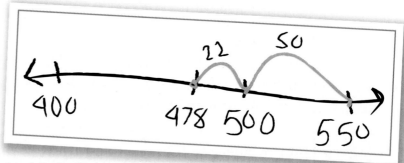

Sample Student Work

After these discussions, you can challenge all or some of the students with this related problem to see if they can generalize their thinking about subtraction to larger numbers:

Now let's say Elena has 500 paper clips and uses 238 of them. How many hundreds are there in the paper clips she has left? How do you know?

Remind students that these estimation strategies can help them get an idea of what a reasonable answer is. Then they can compare their solution with this estimate. It may be helpful for some students to think about this kind of estimation in a money context. That is, every hundred pennies is equivalent to one dollar. The number of hundreds in the difference between the amount of money you have and the price of an object you are planning to buy is the number of dollars to expect in your change.

MATH WORKSHOP

2 Practicing Addition and Subtraction

45 MIN

Students work in pairs on related subtraction problems and continue to play *Capture from 300 to 600* (M10–M11). They should spend some time on both activities, which will continue in Math Workshop in the next session.

2A Related Subtraction Problems

PAIRS

Students solve related subtraction problems on *Student Activity Book* page 11.❶ These problems involve subtracting from 100 and multiples of 100. In Problem Sets 1 and 2, students subtract a number from 100, then subtract the same number from multiples of 100 (e.g., 100 − 93, 300 − 93, 500 − 93).❷ In the last problem, students subtract the same number from a number that is related to the third problem (e.g., 520 − 93).

In Sets 3, 5, and 6, sometimes one number changes and sometimes the other number does (e.g., 300 − 75, 300 − 175, 500 − 175, 540 − 175). In Set 4, students start with 100 − 85; then solve 115 − 85, increasing the difference by 15; then 215 − 85, increasing the difference by 100; and then 215 − 185, which has the same difference as 115 − 85. A number line can help make the relationships among these four problems clear. The ideas underlying the relationships in these problems will be discussed during the next two sessions.

Encourage students to use another piece of paper to explain how they used the relationships among the problems in one set.

Name _____ Date _____

How Many Hundreds? How Many Miles?

Related Subtraction Problems ✏️

As you work on these problems, think about how they are related and how some of the problems help you solve others.

Set 1	Set 2
100 − 90 = _____	100 − 93 = _____
300 − 90 = _____	300 − 93 = _____
330 − 90 = _____	500 − 93 = _____
430 − 90 = _____	520 − 93 = _____

Set 3	Set 4
200 300 500 500 −150 −150 −150 −250	100 − 85 = _____ 115 − 85 = _____ 215 − 85 = _____ 215 − 185 = _____

Set 5	Set 6
300 300 500 540 − 75 −175 −175 −175	200 − 60 = _____ 300 − 60 = _____ 200 − 55 = _____ 300 − 55 = _____

Choose one problem set. On another sheet of paper, explain how you used each problem in the set to solve the next problem.

Sessions 1.3, 1.4   Unit 8 **11**

▲ **Student Activity Book, p. 11** ✏️ WRITING

✔️ ONGOING ASSESSMENT: Observing Students at Work

Students subtract from 100 and multiples of 100, and from numbers near a multiple of 100.

- **Are students seeing and using the relationships among the problems in the set?** For example, do they realize that if they know the answer to 100 − 90, the answer to 300 − 90 will be 200 more? Do they recognize that 215 − 185 will be 100 less than 215 − 85, because 100 more is being subtracted?

- **Do students use tools such as number lines or 100 grids to solve the problems or represent their strategies?**

- **Are students able to use representations, such as a number line, or story contexts to think through the relationships among related problems?**

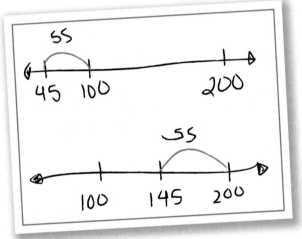

Sample Student Work

As you observe students working, you might ask questions that encourage them to think about story contexts for the number problems. They could use the paper clip context, or another familiar context such as money.

- What if you had 100 dollars and you spent 55 dollars at the grocery store? How much would you have then? What if you had 200 dollars and spent 55? Would you have more money left, or less? How much more did you have to start? So how much more money would you have left?

Students might make sketches, use 100 grids, or draw number lines to help them visualize their story.

Sample Student Work

DIFFERENTIATION: Supporting the Range of Learners

Extension Students who need more of a challenge can extend each set by creating more problems. For example, they might extend Set 5 by writing and solving problems like these:

Set 5

$$
\begin{array}{r} 300 \\ -\ \ 75 \\ \hline \end{array}
\qquad
\begin{array}{r} 300 \\ -175 \\ \hline \end{array}
\qquad
\begin{array}{r} 500 \\ -175 \\ \hline \end{array}
\qquad
\begin{array}{r} 540 \\ -175 \\ \hline \end{array}
$$

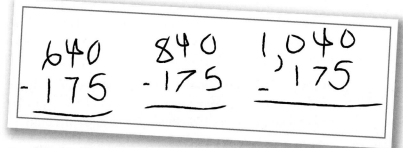

Sample Student Work

2B Capture from 300 to 600

PAIRS

For complete details about this activity, see Session 1.2, pages 37–38.

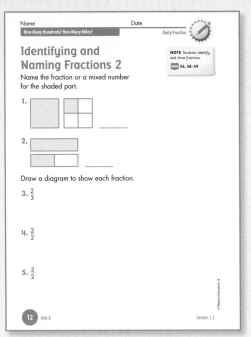

▲ Student Activity Book, p. 12

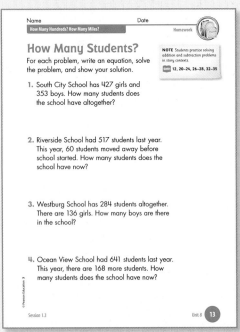

▲ Student Activity Book, p. 13

In this game, players combine positive and negative numbers to make a total that will let them capture a chip.

SESSION FOLLOW-UP

3 Daily Practice and Homework

Daily Practice: For ongoing review, have students complete *Student Activity Book* page 12.

Homework: On *Student Activity Book* page 13, students practice solving addition and subtraction problems in story contexts. You should also encourage students to continue practicing their multiplication combinations.

Student Math Handbook: Students and families may use *Student Math Handbook* pages 32–35 and G1–G2 for reference and review. See pages 179–189 in the back of this unit.

Family Letter: Send home copies of the Family Letter (M19–M20).

Assessment: Multiplication Combinations

Math Focus Points

◆ Using story contexts and representations to support explanations about how changing a number in a subtraction problem affects the difference (e.g., $200 - 75 = 125$ and $200 - 78 = 122$)

◆ Using the relationship of numbers in a subtraction expression to multiples of 100 to solve subtraction problems

◆ Fluently solving multiplication combinations with products to 50

Today's Plan		Materials
① DISCUSSION **Who Has More Paper Clips?** 20 MIN PAIRS CLASS		• M9 (as needed, optional)* • Chart paper with story problem*
② MATH WORKSHOP **Practicing Addition and Subtraction** **2A** More Related Subtraction Problems **2B** More Paper Clip Problems **2C** *Capture from 300 to 600* 30 MIN		**2A** • *Student Activity Book*, pp. 11 and 15 • M9 (as needed, optional)* **2B** • *Student Activity Book*, p. 16 **2C** • Materials from Session 1.2, p. 36
③ ASSESSMENT ACTIVITY **Multiplication Combinations** ✓ 10 MIN INDIVIDUALS		• M21*; M22 (as needed)*
④ SESSION FOLLOW-UP **Daily Practice**		• *Student Activity Book*, p. 17 • *Student Math Handbook*, pp. 32–35, 49–51

*See *Materials to Prepare*, p. 27.

Ten-Minute Math

Counting Around the Class Students count around the class by 2s. Each student says another multiple of 2 until all students have counted once. Highlight the multiples of 2 by writing them on the board as students say them. Ask how many students have counted at 20, 28, and 40. Ask:

• Can anyone think of a multiplication equation that would represent 6 people counting by 2s? ($6 \times 2 = 12$)

Professional Development

❶ **Dialogue Box:** I Know It's Either 2 More or 2 Less, p. 176

DISCUSSION
Who Has More Paper Clips?

20 MIN · PAIRS · CLASS

Math Focus Points for Discussion

◆ Using story contexts and representations to support explanations about how changing a number in a subtraction problem affects the difference (e.g., $200 - 75 = 125$ and $200 - 78 = 122$)

In Unit 3, *Collections and Travel Stories,* students used the context of stickers to consider the question "Who has more?" when comparing two related subtraction expressions (e.g., $90 - 40$ and $90 - 35$). In this discussion, students consider this question in a different context (boxes of paper clips) and with larger numbers. Students may remember and build on their thinking from the earlier unit.❶

Call attention to the problem that you prepared on chart paper.

> Deondra had two boxes of paper clips and used 75 of them to make a wire sculpture. Arthur had two boxes of paper clips and used 78 of them to make a wire sculpture. Who had more paper clips left?

What expression can we write to show Deondra's paper clips? What expression can we write to show Arthur's paper clips?

Write these expressions as students suggest them:

> Deondra's paper clips: $200 - 75$
> Arthur's paper clips: $200 - 78$

Without solving the problems, just look at the numbers and think for a minute about who will have more paper clips left, Deondra or Arthur.

After a minute or two, ask for responses.

Students might say:

"They had the same to begin with, but Arthur used more, so Arthur has less than Deondra."

"Deondra has more because she used less than Arthur."

How do you know? Can you make a sketch to show how you figured it out?

Ask students to work in pairs or individually to make a representation that shows who will have more paper clips left. You might remind students of other representations they have used to show subtraction, such as 100 grids, number lines, or drawings that put paper clips into groups.❷

Students might say:

"I used a number line. They both started out with the same number of paper clips. Deondra used less than Arthur, so her arrow doesn't go back as far as Arthur's and she still has more left."

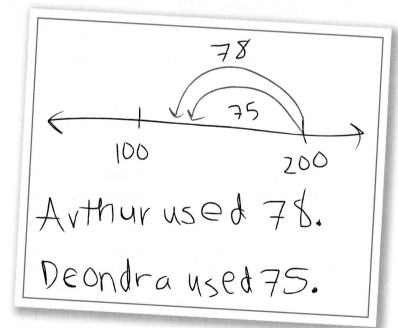

Sample Student Work

Teaching Note

❷ **Using Representations** Using tools such as number lines or story contexts to represent a mathematical situation not only supports students in their computational work but also helps them develop mental images for the operation of subtraction. These mental images for subtraction then become tools for reasoning about the operation itself.

"I used two 100 grids for Deondra and two for Arthur. I knew they both had one full 100 grid that wouldn't change. Then I subtracted 75 on Deondra's other grid and 78 on Arthur's. There were more left on the grid for Deondra, so she had more."

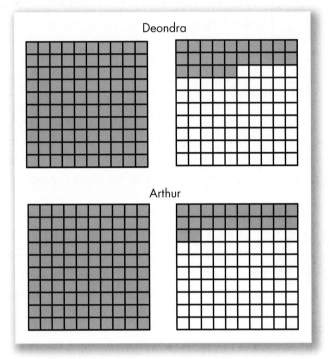

Continue the conversation to consider how many more paper clips Deondra has left than Arthur.

If you know that Deondra has more paper clips because she used fewer, can you figure out from your representations *how many* more she has left?

It will be clear to many students that the number of paper clips Deondra has left will be 3 away from the number that Arthur has left. The more difficult question is: Does Deondra have 3 more or 3 less? Some students' representations might already show the actual number of paper clips each person had left, while others may not. If enough representations show the numbers, go on to have students share their ideas; otherwise give them a few minutes to modify their representations.

Students might say:

"If you count up on the 100 grids how many they have left, you get to Arthur first, and then you have to go three more to Deondra. That means Deondra has 3 more paper clips."

"I put numbers on my number line. I knew 200 minus 75 equaled 125. I could see that Arthur's arrow went back three more than Deondra's, so that's 122."

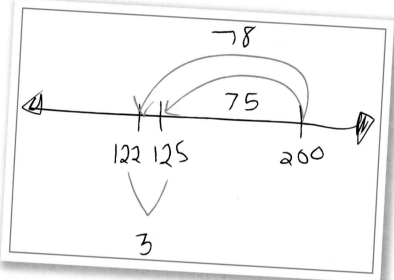

Sample Student Work

What if Deondra had used 80 paper clips and Arthur had used 78? Who has more paper clips left? How many more? How do you know?

Spend another minute or so talking about these questions. Students will continue to work with this idea that the greater the amount subtracted, the smaller the amount remaining, and vice versa, as they solve more related subtraction problems in Math Workshop.

MATH WORKSHOP

30 MIN

② Practicing Addition and Subtraction

Students continue to work on the activities from earlier sessions. Those who have not completed the related subtraction problems on *Student Activity Book* page 11 should do this before continuing with the related problems on page 15. Note that students will be assessed on their

▲ **Student Activity Book, p. 15**

▲ **Student Activity Book, p. 16**

understanding of adding and subtracting multiples of 10 and 100 in the next session. You may decide that some students should spend more time on the *Capture* game in this session, in order to solidify that understanding.

2A More Related Subtraction Problems

PAIRS

The related subtraction problems on *Student Activity Book* page 15 have a slightly different structure than those on page 11, since students do not begin by subtracting from a multiple of 100. For the first problem in each set, they subtract a 2-digit number from either another 2-digit number or a number just over 100 (e.g., 126 − 65). Students should have good strategies for these problems at this point in Grade 3. In the subsequent problems in each set, 100, 200, or 300 is added to the first number in the original expression. For example, Set 2 contains these problems:

$$84 - 28$$

$$184 - 28$$

$$384 - 28$$

In Sets 3 and 4, the second number is also increased by 100 in the third problem (126 − 65, 226 − 65, 226 − 165). Students consider how each of these changes affects the difference.

Encourage students to use representations or story contexts to help them visualize the relationships among the problems in each set. Make available copies of 100 Grids (M9) for students who wish to use them. When students are comparing 93 − 67 and 193 − 67, the number line or 100 grids can illustrate how adding 100 to 93 adds 100 to the difference. When comparing 226 − 65 to 226 − 165, the number line can show how subtracting 100 more from 226 increases the difference by exactly that much.

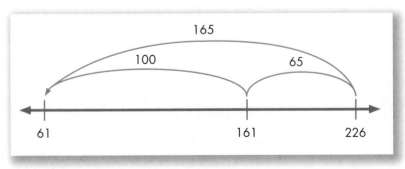

ONGOING ASSESSMENT: Observing Students at Work

Students solve a subtraction problem with 2-digit numbers, or 3-digit numbers slightly over 100, and consider how the difference changes when 100 or a multiple of 100 is added to one of the numbers.

- **What strategies do students use to solve the first problem?** Do they subtract the second number in parts? Do they find the difference between the two numbers by either adding up or subtracting back?

- **Do students recognize that adding some amount to the first number in a subtraction expression (such as 84 − 28) increases the difference by exactly that much?** Do they recognize that adding some amount to the second number decreases the answer by exactly that much?

2B More Paper Clip Problems

PAIRS

On *Student Activity Book* page 16, students solve problems about subtracting from a multiple of 100, similar to the problems they solved in Session 1.1.

For complete details about this activity, see Session 1.1, page 31.

2C Capture from 300 to 600

PAIRS GROUPS

For compete details about this activity, see Session 1.2, pages 37–38.

3 ASSESSMENT ACTIVITY
Multiplication Combinations

10 MIN INDIVIDUALS

With this activity you assess students on Benchmark 5: Demonstrate fluency with multiplication combinations with products up to 50. Students have been practicing these multiplication combinations since their work in Unit 5, *Equal Groups.* Assessment: Multiplication Combinations (M21) is the final assessment on these combinations for the year. ❸

Distribute the assessment sheet to each student. Tell them they have only 2 minutes to solve the problems.

You will want to structure this assessment so that you learn what you need to know without leaving students frustrated that they are not allowed to finish. One approach is to have students complete as many

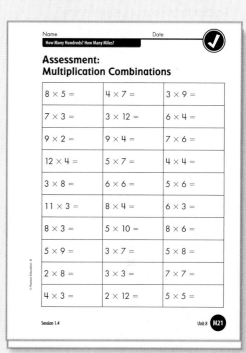

▲ Resource Masters, M21–M22

Teaching Note

4 Explaining the Assessment Since timed work can make some students anxious, talk with them directly about why you want them to solve as many problems as they can in 2 minutes. Explain how that will help both you and them find out which combinations they still need to work on. If students do seem anxious before the assessment, take time to discuss what could help them identify those problems that they can tackle easily.

Professional Development

5 Teacher Note: Learning and Assessing Multiplication Combinations, p. 149

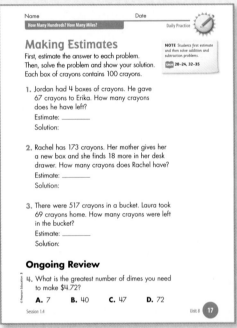

▲ **Student Activity Book, p. 17**

---

problems as they can in 2 minutes, skipping around to answer the ones they "just know" first. At the end of 2 minutes, they stop and circle any problems they have not yet solved, and then continue working. This allows them to finish, yet provides a record of which problems they needed more time to complete. **4**

ONGOING ASSESSMENT: Observing Students at Work

Students demonstrate fluency with multiplication combinations.

- **Are students able to accurately solve multiplication combinations that are presented in a random order?**

- **Are there particular categories of combinations with which students need more practice (e.g., the square number combinations, the × 8 combinations)?**

DIFFERENTIATION: Supporting the Range of Learners

Intervention As needed, cut apart Assessment: Multiplication Combinations (M21) so that students solve fewer problems at one time. While many students will know the majority of these combinations at this point, some students may need an opportunity to take this assessment more than once or to continue practicing a few facts that you can assess individually later on. Use this assessment to determine which combinations students still need to practice and offer them specific practice techniques that are tailored to their needs. **5**

You can use Blank Multiplication Combinations (M22) to create additional assessments, depending on your students' needs. You may use this to assess some students again at any point throughout the rest of the school year, after they have had further opportunities to practice the combinations they still need to learn.

SESSION FOLLOW-UP

4 Daily Practice

 Daily Practice: For reinforcement of this unit's content, have students complete *Student Activity Book* page 17.

Student Math Handbook: Students and families may use *Student Math Handbook* pages 32–35, 49–51 for reference and review. See pages 179–189 in the back of this unit.

Assessment: Operations with Multiples of 10 and 100

Math Focus Points

◆ Subtracting from multiples of 100

◆ Adding multiples of 10 and 100 to, and subtracting them from, 3-digit numbers

◆ Using the relationship of numbers in a subtraction expression to multiples of 100 to solve subtraction problems

Today's Plan		Materials
① DISCUSSION **How Is 215 − 185 Related to 115 − 85?** 15 MIN · PAIRS · CLASS		• Chart paper with story problems*
② ASSESSMENT ACTIVITY **Adding and Subtracting Multiples of 10 and 100** ✔ 20 MIN · INDIVIDUALS		• M23*; M24* ☑
③ MATH WORKSHOP **Practicing Addition and Subtraction** **③A** More Related Subtraction Problems **③B** More Paper Clip Problems 25 MIN		**③A** • *Student Activity Book,* p. 15 • M9 (as needed)* **③B** • *Student Activity Book,* p. 16
④ SESSION FOLLOW-UP **Daily Practice and Homework**		• *Student Activity Book,* pp. 18–19 • *Student Math Handbook,* pp. 32–35; G1–G2

*See *Materials to Prepare,* p. 27.

Ten-Minute Math

Counting Around the Class Students count around the class by 4s. Each student says another multiple of 4 until all students have counted once. Highlight the multiples of 4 by writing them on the board as students say them. Ask:

· How are the multiples of 4 related to the multiples of 2?

· How many students have counted at 24? 48? 80?

· Can anyone think of a multiplication equation that would represent 6 people counting by 4s? ($6 \times 4 = 24$)

15 MIN   PAIRS   CLASS

DISCUSSION

1 How Is 215 − 185 Related to 115 − 85?

Math Focus Points for Discussion

◆ Using the relationship of numbers in a subtraction expression to multiples of 100 to solve subtraction problems

Call attention to the two problems that you prepared on chart paper.

> Becky has one box of paper clips and 15 more. Adam has 85 paper clips. How many more clips does Becky have than Adam?
>
> Pilar has 2 boxes of paper clips and 15 extra. Oscar has one box of paper clips and 85 more. How many more clips does Pilar have than Oscar?

I'd like you to read these two problems and figure out how the second problem is related to the first. Solve both problems and make quick sketches that you can use to explain the relationship between them.

Give students a few minutes to work in pairs. Then ask students to use their pictures to explain their ideas.

If anyone has used a number line, ask that student to show the representation. If not, draw one yourself. Ask students how they can use this representation to compare the two expressions.

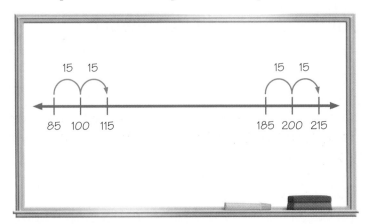

How does this representation help you to think about the way these two problems relate to one another?

Students might say:

"This second problem is just like the other one, except in the first one, 100 is in the middle of the two numbers. In the second, 200 is in the middle of the two numbers. So the answer is the same."

"It doesn't matter what hundreds number is in the middle; it could be 300 or 400 or 500. The answer would still be 30 because you're going 15 above the hundred and 15 below the hundred."

This is an idea that can lead to an important generalization about the properties of subtraction.❶ If a student does not point this out, begin the discussion yourself this way:

Can you think of any other problem that's like these two?

As students suggest other problems, extend the length of the number line so that you have room to place more numbers. Ask them to show on the number line where both numbers could be and what the difference between them would be. For example, if one student suggests 515 − 485 as a similar problem, you might point to the appropriate place on the number line and say:

If I put 500 here, where would 485 be? And where would 515 be? Then what is the difference between 515 and 485?

Algebra Note

❶ **Equivalent Subtraction Expressions** This set of problems involves adding the same amount to each number in a subtraction expression so that the difference remains the same. For example, 115 − 85 = 30, so (115 + 100) − (85 + 100) = 30.

In later years, students might encounter this general idea expressed in symbolic notation as: If $a − b = c$, then $(a + n) − (b + n) = c$. See **Algebra Connections in This Unit,** p. 16.

Algebra Note

② The Relationship Between 115 − 85 and 215 − 85 Students may notice this pattern in these sets of problems: When the first number in a subtraction expression is increased by some amount while the second number stays the same, the difference also increases by that amount. Students might think about this relationship in a story context: "If I have 115 marbles in a bag and I give away 85 of them, I have some number of marbles left in the bag. If I have 115 marbles in one bag and 100 more in another—making a total of 215 marbles—and I give away 85 out of the first bag, I have the same amount left in the first bag as I did before, but I now also have a second bag containing 100 additional marbles." Again, in later years, students might encounter this idea expressed in symbolic notation as: If $a - b = c$, then $(a + n) - b = c + n$.

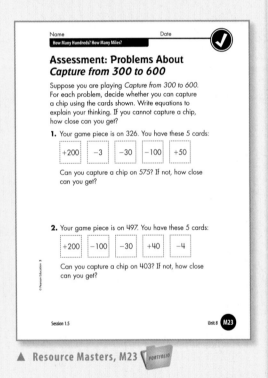

▲ Resource Masters, M23

Students might say:

 "Since it doesn't matter if it's 100 or 200 in the middle, I think it could be 300 in the middle too. 315 − 285."

 "It could be any number of hundreds. One number has to be 15 away to the left on the number line and the other has to be 15 away to the right."

 "You added 100 to the 115 and 100 to the 85, so you could add any number of hundreds to the 115 and the 85. So, it could be 315 − 285, 415 − 385, and so on."

Some students might visualize the relationship among these expressions as sliding the distance between the larger and smaller numbers (in this case, 30) up the number line to a new position.②

ASSESSMENT ACTIVITY

② Adding and Subtracting Multiples of 10 and 100

20 MIN INDIVIDUALS

This assessment addresses Benchmark 1: Add multiples of 10 and 100 (up to 1,000) to and subtract them from any 3-digit number.

Distribute Assessment: Problems About *Capture from 300 to 600* (M23). Students solve two problems based on the game they have been playing throughout this Investigation.

In each of these problems, students work with a given starting point and a given set of Plus/Minus Cards to determine whether they can land on a particular number. For both problems, they write an equation to show how close they can get, and whether they can land on the specified number.

Use Assessment Checklist: Adding and Subtracting Multiples of 10 and 100 (M24) to record information about each student's work. You can make observations as students are working, and also use the checklist as you are reviewing students' papers.

Students should solve these problems without the actual game in front of them to determine whether they can reason about the number relationships in each problem. In Problem 1, students *cannot* get from 326 to 575 with the given cards; the closest they can get is 576 (326 + 200 + 50). In Problem 2, students *can* get from 497 to 403 with these cards: 497 − 100 + 40 − 30 − 4.

At this point in the year, students should be fluent with adding and subtracting multiples of 10 and 100, which means that they can accurately do the computation mentally without counting up or back. They should know that adding or subtracting *just* a multiple of 10 or 100 to a number does not affect the digit in the ones place. In order to meet the benchmark, students should answer both problems correctly. Their computation, as evidenced by the equations they write, should be accurate. They should not have to break up the numbers on the cards into smaller amounts in order to add or subtract (e.g., adding 326 + 200 by counting 426, 526).

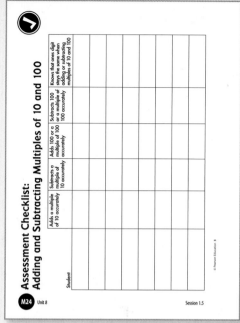

▲ Resource Masters, M24 ✔

ONGOING ASSESSMENT: Observing Students at Work

Students add and subtract multiples of 10 and 100.

- **Can students fluently add and subtract different combinations of the cards?** Do they know how to use the remaining cards to adjust when they are close to a solution?

- **Does the student accurately add and subtract multiples of 10?**

- **Does the student accurately add and subtract multiples of 100?**

- **Does the student recognize that adding and subtracting multiples of 10 and 100 does not change the value of the ones digit?**

- **Is there evidence that the students are using reasoning, rather than trial and error?** That is, in the first problem, do students recognize that they need to add about 200 and some more to get from 326 to 575? For the second problem, do they recognize that they have to subtract some and then add on?

DIFFERENTIATION: Supporting the Range of Learners

Intervention Students who can add or subtract multiples of 10 and 100 but are not consistently accurate should double-check their work. Determine whether these are careless mistakes (such as misreading or miswriting a number) or mistakes that need to be addressed separately.

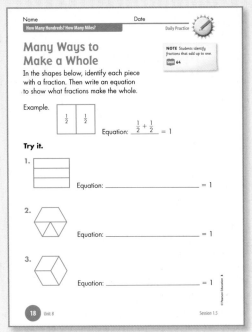

▲ **Student Activity Book, p. 18**

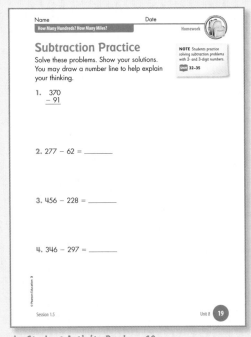

▲ **Student Activity Book, p. 19**

Some students may solve these problems by trial and error, by counting up or back by tens or hundreds. Some students may not understand that the ones digit should not change. These students should continue playing the *Capture* games and practice solving sets of related problems with multiples of 10 and 100.

MATH WORKSHOP

3 Practicing Addition and Subtraction

25 MIN

When students have completed the assessment, they may return to whatever unfinished work they still have from Math Workshop in the previous sessions.

3A More Related Subtraction Problems

PAIRS

For complete details about this activity, see Session 1.4, page 52.

3B More Paper Clip Problems

PAIRS

For complete details about this activity, see Session 1.1, page 31.

SESSION FOLLOW-UP

4 Daily Practice and Homework

 Daily Practice: For ongoing review, have students complete *Student Activity Book* page 18.

 Homework: On *Student Activity Book* page 19, students practice solving subtraction problems with 2- and 3-digit numbers.

 Student Math Handbook: Students and families may use *Student Math Handbook* pages 32–35 and G1–G2 for reference and review. See pages 179–189 in the back of this unit.

Mathematical Emphases

Computational Fluency Adding and subtracting accurately and efficiently

Math Focus Points

◆ Solving addition problems with 3-digit numbers

◆ Estimating and solving addition problems with sums greater than 1,000

◆ Solving addition problems with more than 2 addends

Whole-Number Operations Describing, analyzing, and comparing strategies for adding and subtracting whole numbers

Math Focus Points

◆ Solving addition problems by changing the numbers to create an equivalent problem that is easier to solve

◆ Using story contexts and representations to support explanations about equivalent addition expressions (e.g., $88 + 105 = 90 + 103$)

◆ Identifying addition strategies by focusing on how each strategy starts

Addition Strategies

	Student Activity Book	Student Math Handbook	Professional Development: Read Ahead of Time
SESSION 2.1　　p. 64			
Making an Easier Problem Students examine, represent, and discuss equivalent addition expressions, such as 96 + 145 and 100 + 141.	21	20–24	• **Part 4: Ten-Minute Math and Classroom Routines:** in *Implementing Investigations in Grade 3:* Guess My Rule • **Dialogue Box:** Are These Equal?, p. 178
SESSION 2.2　　p. 72			
Addition Starter Problems Students solve addition problems with 3-digit numbers by using different first steps.	22–26	20–24	
SESSION 2.3　　p. 79			
Categorizing Addition Strategies Students practice solving addition problems with 3-digit numbers. They share and discuss their strategies, classifying them on the basis of how each strategy starts.	27–29	20–24	• **Teacher Note:** Addition Strategies, p. 152
SESSION 2.4　　p. 85			
Adding More Than Two Numbers Students consider a variety of ways to break numbers apart and recombine them when more than two numbers are added and continue to practice adding 3-digit numbers.	30–35	20–24, 25; G8	• **Teacher Note:** Does Order Matter in Addition?, p. 155
SESSION 2.5　　p. 91			
Assessment: Addition Strategies Students discuss how the order of the numbers in a problem with more than two addends affects the sum. They are assessed on their ability to add 3-digit numbers accurately and efficiently.	30–33, 37	20–24, 25	• **Teacher Note:** Assessment: Addition Strategies, p. 156

Materials to Gather	Materials to Prepare
• **Connecting cubes** (as needed) • **Play money** (as needed)	• **Chart paper** Write the problem on page 65 on chart paper. • **M9, 100 Grids** Make copies. (as needed)
• **1,000 charts** (from Unit 3, *Collections and Travel Stories;* if available)	• **M9, 100 Grids** Make copies. (as needed) • **M25–M29, 1,000 Chart** Make copies and assemble in long strips to replace lost charts. (as needed)
• **Chart paper** (2 sheets) • **11″ x 17″ paper** (4–6 sheets)	
• **T100, Combining Collections: How Many Altogether?** • **Collections Cards** (from Unit 3; 1 set per pair)	• **M30,** *Collections Match* Make copies. (as needed) • **M31–M38, Collections Cards** Make copies and cut apart to replace lost cards. (1 set per pair; as needed) • **M39, Combining Collections: How Many Altogether?** Make copies. (as needed)
• **Collections Cards** (from Unit 3 or Session 2.4; 1 set per pair)	• **M39, Combining Collections: How Many Altogether?** Make copies. (as needed) • **M40, Assessment: Addition Strategies** Make copies. (1 per student)

Overhead Transparency

Making an Easier Problem

Math Focus Points

◆ Solving addition problems by changing the numbers to create an equivalent problem that is easier to solve

◆ Using story contexts and representations to support explanations about equivalent addition expressions (e.g., $88 + 105 = 90 + 103$)

Vocabulary
equation
expression
equivalent

Today's Plan		Materials
① DISCUSSION **Are These Equal?**	20 MIN PAIRS CLASS	• Chart paper with story problem*
② ACTIVITY **Making Representations**	20 MIN PAIRS	• M9 (as needed)* • Connecting cubes (as needed); play money (as needed)
③ DISCUSSION **How Do You Know It Is True?**	20 MIN CLASS	
④ SESSION FOLLOW-UP **Daily Practice**		• *Student Activity Book,* p. 21 • *Student Math Handbook,* pp. 20–24

*See *Materials to Prepare,* p. 63.

Ten-Minute Math

Guess My Rule Choose a rule that involves something that students are wearing, such as "wearing red". Select several students who fit the rule to stand in front of the class. Students guess who else fits the rule and who does not, and deduce what the rule is from the evidence. After the rule has been established, ask students:

• How do you know? Is the number of students who fit the rule more or less than half the class?

Students discuss what is about half of the class.

DISCUSSION

1 Are These Equal?

20 MIN   CLASS   PAIRS

Math Focus Points for Discussion

◆ Solving addition problems by changing the numbers to create an equivalent problem that is easier to solve

Call attention to the problem that you prepared on chart paper.

> Mr. Lee's class is collecting pennies for a homeless shelter. On the first day, the third graders bring in 96 pennies. On the second day, they bring in 145 pennies. How much money do they have so far?

Give students a few minutes to solve this problem on their own before sharing their solutions. Circulate to observe what strategies students are using. It is likely that some will break the numbers apart by place value because this strategy is familiar to them. This problem, however, also lends itself to changing the 96 to 100 (or making it a dollar, given that this problem is in the context of money) and adjusting for the change. Look for one or two uses of this strategy to highlight for this discussion.

$$\$0.96 + \$0.04 = \$1.00$$

$$\$1.00 + \$1.41 = \$2.41$$

or

$$100 + 145 = 245$$

$$245 - 4 = 241$$

If no student used a method that involves using 100 in this way, introduce the idea yourself. Write the first step of one of these approaches and ask how this could help solve the problem. Ask questions such as these:

Why did Beatriz add 4 to 96?

What did she do next?

Where did 141 come from?

Do you think this could work with other problems?

After some discussion, write the following on the board or overhead:

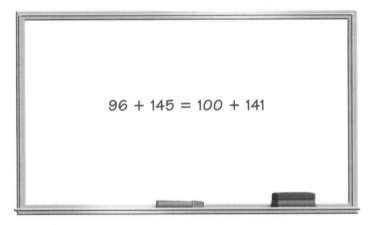

$$96 + 145 = 100 + 141$$

Why do you think this is true—that 96 plus 145 is equal to, or has the same sum as, 100 plus 141? Talk about this with your partner for a minute.

Give students a minute to discuss this equation and then collect several responses. Ask questions that help students describe how the original expression, 96 + 145, was changed to make an equivalent expression.❶

Students might say:

 "If you add 4 to one number, you have to take away the same amount."

Some of you are saying that if you add a certain amount to one addend and subtract the same amount from the other addend, the sum will stay the same. I wonder whether this works for any addition problem. What do you think?

Students will explore this idea further in the next activity.

ACTIVITY

20 MIN   PAIRS

2 Making Representations

Write the following equation on the board or overhead:

$$88 + 105 = 90 + 103$$

What do you notice about this equation? Can you tell that 88 + 105 has the same sum as 90 + 103 without adding the numbers?

I'd like you to work on this with your partner. See whether you can find a way to show how you know that two addition expressions, such as 88 + 105 and 90 + 103, are equal to each other, even before you actually solve both parts of the equation. You may want to try a few more examples as well.

You can use drawings, a number line, or 100 grids to help you, or you can make up a story that shows that they're the same.❷

For the next 20 minutes or so, students work in pairs to represent their thinking about this idea: Is it always true that if you add a certain amount to one addend and subtract the same amount from the other addend, the sum will not change? They should start with the example 88 + 105 = 90 + 103, but they may want to generate other addition expressions to see whether these follow the same "rule."

Have materials available, including connecting cubes and play money. Students will come back together to share their results at the end of the session.

Students use coins to help them represent the equality of two addition expressions.

As students start to work, some may already have a clear idea of why this conjecture is true for any pair of addends, based on their knowledge of how addition works, and they may be ready to begin their representations or stories. Others may see that it works for the particular examples they have done but may not be sure that it will always work. Encourage students to generate more examples and try adding and subtracting different amounts.

Adding and subtracting 2 in the example you just worked out resulted in the same sum. What if you added and subtracted 10: 96 + 145 = 106 + 135? Is the sum still the same?

Algebra Note

❷ **Making Generalizations** Even though students are making arguments for a specific equation (88 + 105 = 90 + 103), they are working on a generalization: If you add 2 to one addend and subtract 2 from the other, the sum remains the same. As they share their representations, their explanations can also show how their arguments apply to any addition problem.

Note that adding and subtracting 10 is probably not something you would do to create an easier problem, but trying such examples helps students think about the general idea of adding and subtracting the same amount.

After students have tried a number of examples, they should make a representation that shows *why* adding an amount to one addend and subtracting the same amount from the other addend results in an expression with the same sum as the original expression.

ONGOING ASSESSMENT: Observing Students at Work

Students use representations to prove that when some amount has been added to one addend in an addition expression and the same amount has been subtracted from the second addend, the sum does not change.

- **Can students articulate clearly the conjecture that they are working on?**

- **Can students generate more examples of this idea?**

- **Can students create a representation or story context that shows how adding and then subtracting the same amount does not change the sum?**

DIFFERENTIATION: Supporting the Range of Learners

Intervention If some students do not know how to get started on creating a representation or a story context, ask them first to represent, or create a story for, 88 + 105, just as they might create a story for any addition problem.

- What's a story problem for 88 + 105?

- What would happen in the story if 88 changed to 90?

- How would 105 change if you subtracted the same amount you just added to 88? What would happen in the story?

- Your story about fish in two tanks shows that 88 + 105 has the same sum as 90 + 103. What if there were different numbers of fish in the two tanks at the beginning?

- Can you use your story to show how this would work with different numbers?

DISCUSSION

3 How Do You Know It Is True?

20 MIN   CLASS

Math Focus Points for Discussion

◆ Using story contexts and representations to support explanations about equivalent addition expressions (e.g., $88 + 105 = 90 + 103$)

Bring the class together when there are about 20 minutes left in the session. Have pairs of students share the representations or story situations they used to show the equivalent relationship between the two expressions $88 + 105$ and $90 + 103$.

As students are sharing, look for ways in which students' representations show that when one number in the expression is increased, the other number must be decreased by the same amount in order to maintain the same sum.

Students might say:

"Here's my story. I have 88 baseball cards in one box and 105 cards in another box. If I take 2 cards out of the second box and put them in with the cards in the first box, I end up with 90 and 103. But I still have the same number of cards altogether, as long as I didn't lose any in between."

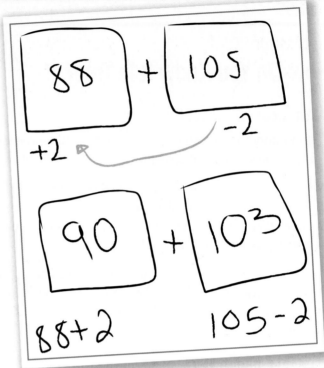

Sample Student Work

 "I used a number line to show that 88 + 105 is the same as 90 + 103."

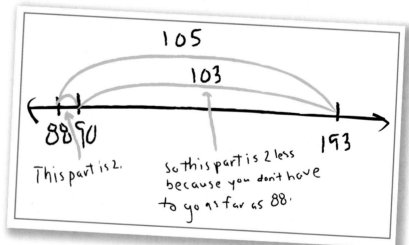

Sample Student Work

Ask students to consider whether this idea works for other numbers. Write the following expression on the board or overhead:

$$85 + 145$$

How could you change this expression to make an **equivalent** expression that is easier to add?

Give students one more equation to consider:

$$96 + 114$$

This discussion is just the beginning of the work that students will continue to do over the next couple of years with creating easier equivalent expressions in order to solve computation problems. It is not expected at this point that third graders will necessarily adopt this strategy, but these discussions provide the opportunity for them to consider how the operation of addition works and to deepen their understanding of the operation.

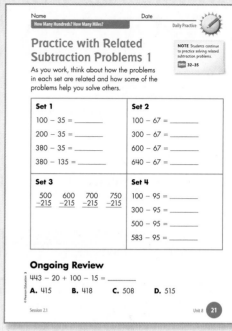

Name _____ **Date** _____

How Many Hundreds? How Many Miles? | *Daily Practice*

Practice with Related Subtraction Problems 1

NOTE Students continue to practice solving related subtraction problems.
SMH 32–35

As you work, think about how the problems in each set are related and how some of the problems help you solve others.

Set 1
100 − 35 = _____
200 − 35 = _____
380 − 35 = _____
380 − 135 = _____

Set 2
100 − 67 = _____
300 − 67 = _____
600 − 67 = _____
640 − 67 = _____

Set 3
500 −215 600 −215 700 −215 750 −215

Set 4
100 − 95 = _____
300 − 95 = _____
500 − 95 = _____
583 − 95 = _____

Ongoing Review
443 − 20 + 100 − 15 = _____
A. 415 B. 418 C. 508 D. 515

Session 2.1   Unit 8   21

▲ **Student Activity Book, p. 21**

SESSION FOLLOW-UP
Daily Practice

 Daily Practice: For reinforcement of this unit's content, have students complete *Student Activity Book* page 21.

Student Math Handbook: Students and families may use *Student Math Handbook* pages 20–24 for reference and review. See pages 179–189 in the back of this unit.

Addition Starter Problems

Math Focus Points

◆ Solving addition problems with 3-digit numbers

◆ Estimating and solving addition problems with sums greater than 1,000

◆ Identifying addition strategies by focusing on how each strategy starts

Vocabulary
estimate

Today's Plan				Materials
1 ACTIVITY **Revisiting Addition Starter Problems**		15 MIN	INDIVIDUALS CLASS	
2 ACTIVITY **Addition Starter Problems**		35 MIN	INDIVIDUALS	• *Student Activity Book*, pp. 22–24 • M9 (as needed)*
3 DISCUSSION **Crossing Over 1,000**		10 MIN	CLASS	• 1,000 Charts (optional)*
4 SESSION FOLLOW-UP **Daily Practice and Homework**				• *Student Activity Book*, pp. 25–26 • *Student Math Handbook*, pp. 20–24

*See *Materials to Prepare*, p. 63.

Ten-Minute Math

Guess My Rule Choose a rule that describes a physical characteristic, such as "shoulder-length hair". Select several students who fit the rule to stand in front of the class. Students guess who else fits the rule and who does not, and deduce what the rule is from the evidence. After the rule has been established, ask students:

• Is the number of students who fit the rule more or less than half the class? How do you know?

Students discuss what is about half of the class.

ACTIVITY

1 Revisiting Addition Starter Problems

15 MIN INDIVIDUALS CLASS

Show students the following problem, and ask them to estimate about how much the sum would be:

$$379 + 412 =$$

First of all, about how many hundreds will the answer have? What do you have to pay attention to in order to know how many hundreds? What do the 79 and the 12 tell you about how many hundreds there will be?

Students should be able to look at the 3 hundreds in 379 and the 4 hundreds in 412 to see that there are at least 7 hundreds in the sum. They also should know that there will be a little less than one more hundred because the sum of $79 + 12$ is close to 100.

Below the problem, write three starter problems. Remind students that they solved problems like these when they worked on addition earlier in the year.

$$379 + 412 =$$

$$300 + 400 =$$
$$379 + 400 =$$
$$379 + 1 =$$

Here are three different ways you could start to solve the problem $379 + 412$. Which one of these makes it easiest for you to solve the problem? Choose one of these starter problems, and think about how you would finish the problem. Write your strategy to keep track of it, and then we'll share your ideas.

Give students a few minutes to solve $379 + 412$ with the starter problem of their choice, either individually or with a partner. When most students have finished, briefly collect one solution for each start. Help students describe what they did, using language that identifies what is happening mathematically in each strategy.

Student Activity Book, p. 22

Name _____ **Date** _____

How Many Hundreds? How Many Miles?

Addition Starter Problems (page 1 of 3)

In each set, solve all three starter problems.
Then solve the final problem. Show your solution.
Use one of the starter problems to help you.

Set 1

100 + 600 = _____   150 + 650 = _____   152 + 600 = _____

Final problem: **152 + 683** = _____

Show your solution.

Set 2

400 + 200 = _____   429 + 200 = _____   430 + 200 = _____

Final problem: **429 + 266** = _____

Show your solution.

22   Unit 8   Session 2.2

© Pearson Education 3

▲ **Student Activity Book, p. 22**

Which starter problem did you use? Tell me about your next steps.

Students might say:

"I started with 379 + 400. I broke the 412 into 400 + 10 + 2 and added each part on."

(Sample Student Work)

$$379 + 400 = 779$$
$$779 + 10 = 789$$
$$789 + 2 = 791$$

Sample Student Work

"I used 300 + 400. I broke the numbers 379 and 412 into hundreds, tens, and ones: 300 + 70 + 9 and 400 + 10 + 2. Then I added each part."

$$300 + 400 = 700$$
$$70 + 10 = 80$$
$$9 + 2 = 11$$
$$700 + 80 + 11 = 791$$

Sample Student Work

Did anyone start with 379 + 1? That changes the number to 380, which might be easier to work with. Where did the 1 come from? What did you have left to add after that?

This strategy might look like one of these:

$$379 + 412$$

$$379 + 1 = 380 \qquad\qquad 379 + 1 = 380$$

$$380 + 411 = 791 \qquad\qquad 380 + 412 = 792$$

$$792 - 1 = 791$$

Some students may relate this problem to the work they did in the last session, that is, they might notice that when they add 1 to 379, they can make the equivalent expression 379 + 412 = 380 + 411.

Do not spend much time discussing these strategies at this point. For now, just collect an example of each. Students work on more starter problems for the rest of the session.

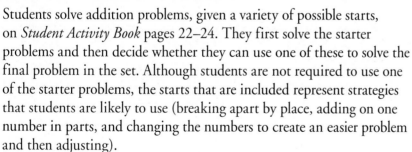

ACTIVITY

2 Addition Starter Problems

35 MIN | INDIVIDUALS

Students solve addition problems, given a variety of possible starts, on *Student Activity Book* pages 22–24. They first solve the starter problems and then decide whether they can use one of these to solve the final problem in the set. Although students are not required to use one of the starter problems, the starts that are included represent strategies that students are likely to use (breaking apart by place, adding on one number in parts, and changing the numbers to create an easier problem and then adjusting).

These problems have larger numbers than students worked with when they first encountered starter problems earlier in the year. In Sets 4 and 6, the sum is greater than 1,000. Students will discuss combining 3-digit numbers that result in a sum over 1,000 at the end of the session. Make sure that all students have worked on Set 4 before you begin the discussion.❶

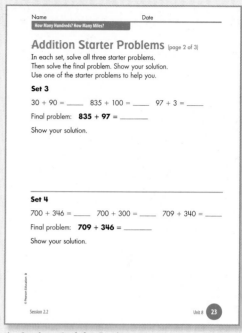

▲ Student Activity Book, p. 23

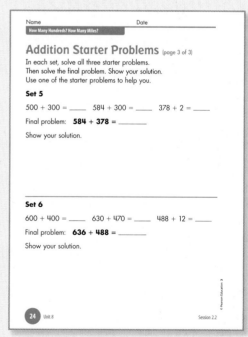

▲ Student Activity Book, p. 24

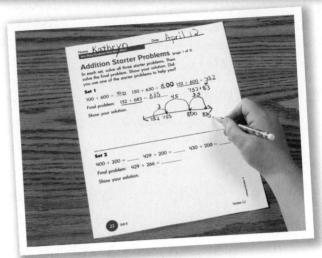

Students may use number lines to show their solutions to addition problems.

ONGOING ASSESSMENT: Observing Students at Work

Students consider three different approaches to solving addition problems.

- **Can students solve the starter problems mentally (i.e., they write the answers without doing paper-and-pencil computation)?**

- **Do students choose one of the starts to solve the final problem?** Which one? Do they have another efficient way to start?

- **Can students follow through with the solution and keep track of their steps?**

- **Are students' solutions accurate?**

DIFFERENTIATION: Supporting the Range of Learners

Intervention If some students find these numbers too difficult to work with at first, you may change some of the numbers to smaller 3-digit numbers. Encourage students to use 100 grids as a representation for how many hundreds are in the addends and therefore in the sum.

Extension Students who finish early may solve some of the problems in a second way, choosing a different start. You may also offer them a new problem and ask them to make up three different starter problems for it.

DISCUSSION

③ Crossing Over 1,000

10 MIN   CLASS

Math Focus Points for Discussion

◆ Estimating and solving addition problems with sums greater than 1,000

When students first encounter problems with sums over 1,000, they have to extend the strategies they have used for adding 10s to adding 100s. Until now, they have thought about the number of 10s that add to 100. Now, they must think about the number of 100s that would add to 1,000.

Refer students to the final problem in Set 4 on *Student Activity Book* page 23: 709 + 346.

Some of you noticed that the numbers in this problem are bigger than the numbers you've been adding until now. Let's look at a similar problem. What is your estimate for the answer to this problem?

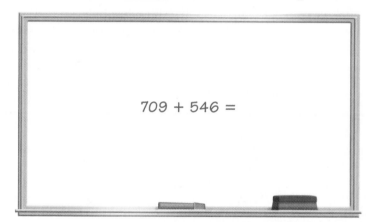

709 + 546 =

The important point is that there are 12 hundreds in the answer because there are 7 hundreds in 709 and 5 in 546. Students should also know that "1 thousand 2 hundred" is the same as 12 hundreds.

If students are having trouble thinking about 100s this way, you might refer them to their 1,000 chart from Unit 3, *Collections and Travel Stories*. They will see that adding 3 pages of 100 to seven pages of 100 uses up the entire 1,000 chart and that they still need two more 100s. They may use a second 1,000 chart (M25–M29) to represent the rest of the sum (255).

If students need more work with the idea of adding 100s and reaching 1,000, you may want to pose some additional problems with different numbers of 100s.

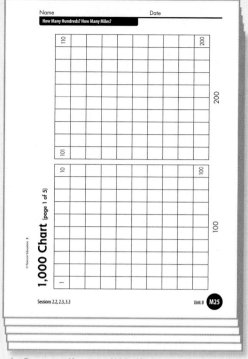

▲ **Resource Masters, M25–M29**

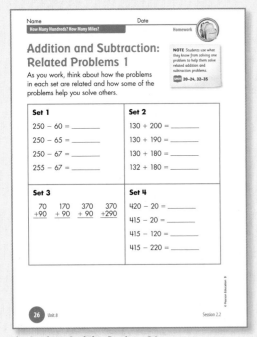

▲ Student Activity Book, p. 25

▲ Student Activity Book, p. 26

What if I changed the problem to 1,009 + 546? Can you use the last problem to help you figure out this one?

Students may think of this problem in two ways, one that uses the previous problem and one that does not.

Students might say:

"1,009 has 300 more than 709, so the answer would have 3 more hundreds, so that's 15 hundreds."

"1,009 has 10 hundreds and 546 has 5 hundreds, so there are 15 hundreds in all."

Remind students that 15 hundreds can also be named "1 thousand 5 hundred."

You may also challenge the class with some problems that reach 1,000 because an additional 100 is made from the sum of the numbers in the tens and ones places. For example, 463 + 552 has an answer over 1,000, even though 400 + 500 is only 900.

SESSION FOLLOW-UP

4 Daily Practice and Homework

 Daily Practice: For ongoing review, have students complete *Student Activity Book* page 25.

 Homework: On *Student Activity Book* page 26, students solve sets of related problems that include both addition and subtraction.

 Student Math Handbook: Students and families may use *Student Math Handbook* pages 20–24 for reference and review. See pages 179–189 in the back of this unit.

Categorizing Addition Strategies

Math Focus Points

◆ Solving addition problems with 3-digit numbers

◆ Identifying addition strategies by focusing on how each strategy starts

Today's Plan			Materials
① ACTIVITY **Solving Addition Problems**	🕐 40 MIN	🚶 INDIVIDUALS	• *Student Activity Book*, pp. 27–28
② DISCUSSION **Categorizing Addition Strategies**	🕐 20 MIN	👥 CLASS	• Chart paper; 11″ x 17″ paper
③ SESSION FOLLOW-UP **Daily Practice**			• *Student Activity Book*, p. 29 • *Student Math Handbook*, pp. 20–24

Ten-Minute Math

Guess My Rule Choose a rule that describes a type of animal such as "Animals that live in the desert". Inside a large circle, write the names of several animals that fit the rule. As students suggest animals that may or may not fit this rule, place them inside or outside the circle. Students deduce what the rule is from the evidence. After the rule has been established, ask students:

· Is the number of animals that fit the rule more or less than half the total? How do you know?

Students discuss what is about half of the total.

Differentiation

1 **English Language Learners** If you identify English Language Learners who have work you want shared, give them the chance to share their strategies with you or a small group before the whole-class discussion. This will allow you to review terms as needed and provide the students with any language support required for their presentation. During the discussion, plan to check frequently to make sure that all English Language Learners understand other students' explanations. Paraphrase as necessary to simplify students' responses.

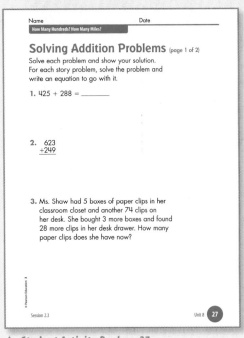

▲ **Student Activity Book, p. 27**

ACTIVITY

Solving Addition Problems

40 MIN INDIVIDUALS

On *Student Activity Book* pages 27–28, students practice solving problems with 3-digit numbers, including some with sums that are greater than 1,000.

There are six problems for you to solve today. Look closely at the numbers before you start to solve each problem, and think about the strategies we have been talking about. After you have spent some time on these, we'll come back together and share our strategies for Problem 2.

ONGOING ASSESSMENT: Observing Students at Work

Students solve addition problems with 3-digit numbers.

- **Do students break the numbers apart in reasonable and efficient ways to solve these problems?** Do they recombine them accurately?

- **Do students recognize number relationships that can help them make the problem easier to solve?** For example, do they change 249 to 250 in Problem 2 or notice that 74 + 28 is close to 75 + 25 in Problem 3?

- **Can students record their solutions clearly, using mathematical notation?**

At this point in the year, students should be familiar and competent with at least one strategy for solving an addition problem by breaking the numbers apart in some reasonable and efficient way, a benchmark for the previous addition and subtraction unit.

Several of these problems also lend themselves to strategies that involve changing the numbers to create an easier problem, particularly Problems 2 and 6. As you observe students working, look for examples of strategies that make use of this idea, as well as examples of the "breaking numbers apart" strategies that students may be more familiar with (i.e., by place value, by adding on one number in parts, or by combining parts to make a multiple of 10 or 100).

For the discussion of Problem 2 that follows, look for several students whose strategies are clear and represent the variety in the classroom. Ask them to be prepared to share their work.**1**

DIFFERENTIATION: Supporting the Range of Learners

Intervention Students who are still working on a reliable addition strategy for multidigit numbers should focus on one strategy and have opportunities to practice it. For many students the most accessible strategy, which can be used with any set of numbers, is to break the numbers apart by place value. Ask questions to help students identify the place value parts of the problem.

- Where are the hundreds in this problem? How many will there be altogether if you combine them?

- After you combine the hundreds, what's left to add? How would you break those numbers apart by place value?

Encourage students to use place-value sketches (such as stickers) if that helps them visualize the value of each number. Help students set this strategy up in such a way that all the parts of the numbers are clear to them and they can keep track of what they have to add to get their final answer.

$$425 + 288 =$$
$$400 + 200 = 600$$
$$20 + 80 = 100$$
$$5 + 8 = 13$$
$$\overline{425 + 288 = 713}$$

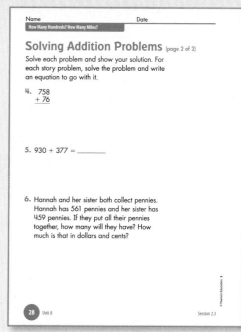

▲ Student Activity Book, p. 28

DISCUSSION

20 MIN   CLASS

2 Categorizing Addition Strategies

Math Focus Points for Discussion

◆ Identifying addition strategies by focusing on how each strategy starts

When there are about 20 minutes left in the session, bring the class together to share their strategies for Problem 2, 623 + 249.

Yesterday, while using starter problems, we talked about different ways you can start out when you're doing addition. Now we're going to look at some of the ways that people in our class started to solve Problem 2.

Call on the students whom you identified while observing the previous activity, and collect the starter problems that represent several different strategies. As they explain their approaches, write each starter problem on a different sheet of 11″ x 17″ paper and tape them to the board.

$$600 + 200 = 800$$

$$623 + 200 = 823$$

$$249 + 1 = 250$$

$$620 + 240 = 860$$

We've been talking about different ways to solve addition problems. One of these ways is to break the numbers apart. When you look up here, which of these strategies starts by breaking the numbers apart?

On a piece of chart paper, write the title "Break the Numbers Apart." As students identify a strategy that begins by breaking numbers apart, tape that smaller sheet to the new chart. In the examples above, most of which should be represented in your classroom, all but $249 + 1$ involve breaking the numbers apart in some way. Students may argue that $249 + 1$ is also a "breaking apart" strategy, if they are thinking of the 1 as coming from 623 and thus see that 623 was broken apart into $622 + 1$. Give students a few minutes to discuss this, and then offer a second category for them to consider.

Another kind of addition strategy we've been talking about is to change the numbers to make an easier problem to solve. Do you think any of these starts fall into that category?

On another piece of chart paper, write the title "Change the Numbers," and move particular strategy sheets onto this one as students suggest. Again, listen to students' arguments for identifying $249 + 1$ as a "changing the numbers" strategy.

Students might say:

"There's no 250 in the problem to start with, so you have to add 1 to make it a different number that's easier. Then you have to take the 1 away at the end, because it's not supposed to be there."

Also offer the following possibility as a way to change the numbers, if it has not already been suggested:

Could I make this problem 625 + 250? That's pretty easy, because many of us know 25 plus 50 in our heads. What did I do to the numbers to change them this time? What would I have to do to get the correct sum?

After the class has decided which starts are "break the numbers apart" strategies and which are "change the numbers" strategies, ask the students who offered these strategies to tell you how they carried out the rest of the solution, and record these on the charts.

Break the Numbers Apart
623 + 249

Adding by place value
600 + 200 = 800
20 + 40 = 60
3 + 9 = 12

800 + 60 + 12 = 872

Adding by place value (by tens)
620 + 240 = 860
3 + 9 = 12
860 + 12 = 872

Adding one number in parts
623 + 200 = 823
823 + 40 = 863
863 + 9 = 872

Change the Numbers
623 + 249

249 + 1 = 250
623 + 250 = 873
873 − 1 = 872

Math Note

❷ The U.S. Standard Algorithm Some students in your class may be familiar with the U.S. standard algorithm, sometimes called the "carrying" or regrouping algorithm. It is efficient, but exactly what makes it efficient—its compactness of notation—also obscures the place value of the numbers and the logic of the steps of the procedure. Too often, students learn to operate with single digits and lose their sense of the meaning of the numbers. Students who can explain to you the logic of each step and the meaning of its shorthand notation can certainly continue using this procedure. They should also learn other strategies in order to expand their understanding of the operation of addition. Students will study this algorithm in Grade 4 *after* they have developed efficient and accurate addition strategies based on their understanding of the operation of addition and the base-ten number system.

Professional Development

❸ Teacher Note: Addition Strategies, p. 152

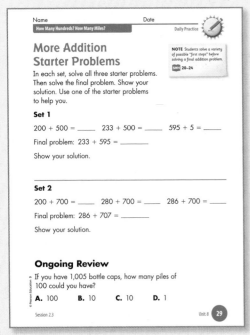

▲ Student Activity Book, p. 29

Spend the last few minutes discussing the differences among the strategies that break the numbers apart. At this point, students should be familiar with the language of "adding by place" and "adding one number in parts" and should be able to identify which strategy is which. Some students may recognize that a strategy that begins with $620 + 240$ is also a place-value strategy, and they may notice that they are adding all of the tens (62 tens plus 24 tens). Students will continue to examine and classify the types of addition strategies in Grade 4.❷ ❸

For the rest of this unit, keep these charts posted so that students may refer to them as they continue to practice solving addition problems.

SESSION FOLLOW-UP
3 Daily Practice

 Daily Practice: For reinforcement of this unit's content, have students complete *Student Activity Book* page 29.

 Student Math Handbook: Students and families may use *Student Math Handbook* pages 20–24 for reference and review. See pages 179–189 in the back of this unit.

Adding More Than Two Numbers

Math Focus Points

◆ Solving addition problems with more than 2 addends

◆ Solving addition problems with 3-digit numbers

Today's Plan		Materials
1 **ACTIVITY** **Introducing Multiple-Addend Problems**	15 MIN INDIVIDUALS CLASS	
2 **MATH WORKSHOP** **Practicing Addition** **2A** Multiple-Addend Problems **2B** More Addition Problems **2C** Collections Match	45 MIN	**2A** • *Student Activity Book,* pp. 30–31 **2B** • *Student Activity Book,* p. 32 **2C** • *Student Activity Book,* p. 33 • M30*; M31–M38*; M39* • T100
3 **SESSION FOLLOW-UP** **Daily Practice and Homework**		• *Student Activity Book,* pp. 34–35 • *Student Math Handbook,* pp. 20–24, 25; G8

*See *Materials to Prepare,* p. 63.

Ten-Minute Math

Guess My Rule Choose a rule that describes a type of object such as "things you play sports with". Inside a large circle, write the names of several things that fit the rule. As students suggest objects that may or may not fit this rule, place them inside or outside the circle. Students deduce what the rule is from the evidence. After the rule has been established, ask students:

• Is the number of objects that fit the rule more or less than half the total? How do you know?

Students discuss what is about half of the total.

Student Activity Book, p. 30 and p. 31

Name   Date

How Many Hundreds? How Many Miles?

Adding More Than
Two Numbers (page 1 of 2)

For each problem, first estimate about how many
hundreds the answer will have. Then solve the
problem and show your solution.

1. 343 + 487 + 55 = _____

   About how many hundreds? _____

   Solution:

2. 145 + 628 + 37 = _____

   About how many hundreds? _____

   Solution:

3. 245 + 386 + 465 = _____

   About how many hundreds? _____

   Solution:

30   Unit 8   Sessions 2.4, 2.5

© Pearson Education 3

▲ **Student Activity Book, p. 30**

Name   Date

How Many Hundreds? How Many Miles?

Adding More Than
Two Numbers (page 2 of 2)

For each problem, first estimate about how many
hundreds the answer will have. Then solve the
problem and show your solution.

4. 801 + 27 + 446 = _____

   About how many hundreds? _____

   Solution:

5. 78 + 296 + 813 = _____

   About how many hundreds? _____

   Solution:

6. 190 + 791 + 359 = _____

   About how many hundreds? _____

   Solution:

© Pearson Education 3

Session 2.4, 2.5   Unit 8   31

▲ **Student Activity Book, p. 31**

ACTIVITY

1 Introducing Multiple-Addend Problems

15 MIN   INDIVIDUALS   CLASS

Write the following problem on the board:

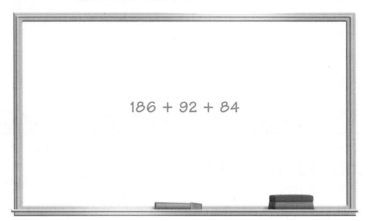

$$186 + 92 + 84$$

Here's an addition problem with more than two numbers. Let's estimate this first before we solve it. About how many hundreds do you think the answer will have?

Students' responses are likely to range from 100 (because they see only 1 hundred) to 400. As students give their estimates, ask them to explain their reasoning. Listen for explanations that include thinking of 92 and 84 as each being close to 100, and 186 as being close to 200, making the sum about 400 altogether. Some students may recognize that because each of these numbers is less than the nearest hundred, the sum will be less than 400, so a number in the 300s is a good estimate.

Ask students to solve the problem for an exact answer, either by themselves or with a partner. They may keep track of their thinking on blank paper. When most students have finished, collect a few solutions. Focus the sharing on how students broke the numbers apart and recombined them.

- Jane, you started with 186 + 84, even though that's not the order the numbers are written in. What made you decide to start there?

- Zhang, it looks like you added all the tens first. What did you have left to do after that?

- Denzel, when you added 186 plus 14 to get to 200, how were you thinking about solving the problem?

Listen for solutions that involve combining the numbers, or parts of the numbers, out of order. Although you can expect third graders to understand that when adding two numbers, they can switch the order of the numbers without affecting the sum (3 + 5 = 8 and 5 + 3 also equals 8), reordering the numbers when there are multiple addends may be a new idea for some students. This idea will be discussed in the next session after students have had a chance to work on solving multiple-addend problems on their own. ❶ ❷

MATH WORKSHOP

② Practicing Addition

45 MIN

Students work on three activities that involve practice with addition. They solve multiple-addend problems, solve more problems with 3-digit numbers, and revisit an addition game, *Collections Match*, from Unit 3.

· ·

②A Multiple-Addend Problems

INDIVIDUALS

On *Student Activity Book* pages 30–31, students first estimate the number of hundreds in the solution, and then solve each problem. They should get to at least Problem 3 because this will be discussed at the beginning of the next session. They will have a chance to finish these pages in the next session's Math Workshop.

ONGOING ASSESSMENT: Observing Students at Work

Students solve addition problems with more than two addends.

- **Can students accurately estimate how many hundreds the answer will have?** Do they consider how the tens and ones digits affect the number of hundreds as well as the hundreds digits?

- **How do students reorder and break the numbers apart?** Do they look for combinations that they can easily solve, such as combinations that make 10 or 100?

- **Do students keep track of all the parts of the numbers and recombine them accurately?**

Math Note

❶ **Adding in Any Order** In earlier grades, students discussed the idea that pairs of numbers can be added in either order, which is the commutative property of addition (e.g., 5 + 8 = 8 + 5). With multiple-addend problems, they are also making use of another property of addition, the associative property. It is not useful for students at this age to name these properties or sort out which of the two properties they are using. Rather, they should focus on the overall generalization that changing the order of addends in an addition expression does not affect the sum, no matter how many addends are involved.

Professional Development

❷ **Teacher Note:** Does Order Matter in Addition?, p. 155

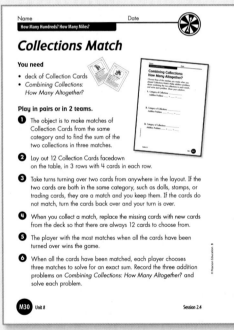

▲ **Student Activity Book, p. 32**

The Student Activity Book page shows:

Name _____ Date _____

How Many Hundreds? How Many Miles?

More Addition Problems

Solve each problem and show your solution.

1. 451 + 546 = _____	2. 316 + 490 = _____
3. 298 + 548 = _____	4. 135 + 821 = _____
5. 276 + 765 = _____	6. 386 + 331 = _____
7. 502 + 799 = _____	8. 738 + 834 = _____

32   Unit 8   Sessions 2.4, 2.5

The Resource Masters page shows:

Name _____ Date _____

How Many Hundreds? How Many Miles?

Collections Match

You need
- deck of Collection Cards
- *Combining Collections: How Many Altogether?*

Play in pairs or in 2 teams.

1. The object is to make matches of Collection Cards from the same category and to find the sum of the two collections in three matches.

2. Lay out 12 Collection Cards facedown on the table, in 3 rows with 4 cards in each row.

3. Take turns turning over two cards from anywhere in the layout. If the two cards are both in the same category, such as dolls, stamps, or trading cards, they are a match and you keep them. If the cards do not match, turn the cards back over and your turn is over.

4. When you collect a match, replace the missing cards with new cards from the deck so that there are always 12 cards to choose from.

5. The player with the most matches when all the cards have been turned over wins the game.

6. When all the cards have been matched, each player chooses three matches to solve for an exact sum. Record the three addition problems on *Combining Collections: How Many Altogether?* and solve each problem.

M30   Unit 8   Session 2.4

▲ **Resource Masters, M30**

DIFFERENTIATION: Supporting the Range of Learners

Intervention For some students, keeping track of the parts of the numbers that they have already used can be an organizational challenge. Help them devise some system, such as crossing out digits as the numbers they represent are added or writing out each number by place value, so that they can check whether they have included each place somewhere in their computation.

2B More Addition Problems

INDIVIDUALS

The set of problems on *Student Activity Book* page 32 provides further practice of the addition strategies that students have been working with.

ONGOING ASSESSMENT: Observing Students at Work

Students practice solving addition problems with 3-digit numbers.

- **Do students choose a strategy for each problem that they can use efficiently?** Do they use the same strategy for each problem, or do they choose different strategies based on the number relationships they see in the problem?

- **Are the students' computations accurate?** Do they clearly keep track of all the steps in their solutions?

DIFFERENTIATION: Supporting the Range of Learners

Students need not solve all of these problems. Encourage students to first look at the whole set and then choose problems that look like the right level of challenge for them.

Intervention Some students may choose to work on only the problems that have smaller numbers. Encourage these students to model these problems as needed.

Extension Some students may focus on problems that lend themselves to a strategy that they would like to explore further. For example, if some students seem particularly interested in trying to make equivalent addition expressions, they might start with Problems 2, 3, or 7.

2C *Collections Match*

PAIRS

As needed, remind students of the game *Collections Match*, which they played in Unit 3, *Collections and Travel Stories*. Students can review the rules for this game on *Collections Match* (M30). If students need a reminder of how to use the recording sheet, show them Combining Collections: How Many Altogether? (T100).

Students use their decks of Collection Cards (M31–M38) to generate and then solve addition problems with 2- and 3-digit numbers. The game is similar to other match games that students may be familiar with. Twelve cards are laid facedown on the table. Players turn over two cards, trying to match collections in the same category, such as toys, sports, or animals. Students first play the game to collect their matches; the winner is the player who makes the most matches. Students then choose three pairs from the matches they made and write addition problems about combining the collections in each pair. They record and solve these problems on *Student Activity Book* page 33. As students use up this page, make available copies of Combining Collections: How Many Altogether? (M39).

Constructing and solving addition problems in Collections Match *reinforces addition skills.*

Remind students that the activity includes both playing the game and solving the problems they choose after they finish the game. Encourage students to choose problems that give them an appropriate level of challenge; that is, not too easy and not too hard.

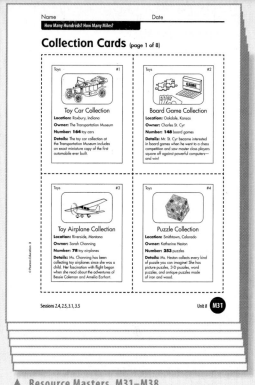

▲ **Resource Masters, M31–M38**

▲ **Student Activity Book, p. 33; Resource Masters, M39; T100**

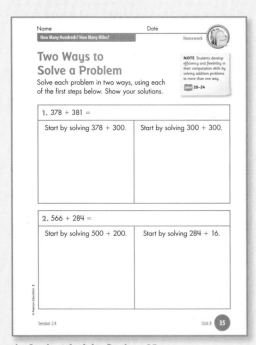

▲ **Student Activity Book, p. 34**

The following appears on Student Activity Book p. 34:

Name _____ Date _____

How Many Hundreds? How Many Miles?

Daily Practice

How Can We Share?

Solve each problem. Draw pictures to help you explain your answer.

NOTE Students find ways to divide a group of objects equally.

Unit 47, 48

1. How can 6 people share 8 hot dogs?

2. How can 5 people share 10 pencils?

3. How can 6 people share $3.00?

4. How can 6 people share 3 granola bars?

Ongoing Review

5. Which expression is more than 1,000?

   A. 833 + 150　　**C.** 556 + 424

   B. 899 + 119　　**D.** 378 + 602

34　Unit 8　　Session 2.4

ONGOING ASSESSMENT: Observing Students at Work

Students solve addition problems with 2- and 3-digit numbers.

- **Do students have at least one strategy that they can use effectively, such as adding by place or adding on one number in parts?**

- **Do students break the numbers apart in efficient ways, either by place value, by making use of multiples of 10 and 100, or by using combinations that make 10 or 100?**

- **Do students change the numbers to make an easier addition expression for problems that lend themselves to this strategy?** Can they make the adjustment accurately?

- **Do students keep track of the steps in their solutions?**

- **Are students' computations accurate?**

The following appears on Student Activity Book p. 35:

Name _____ Date _____

How Many Hundreds? How Many Miles?

Homework

Two Ways to Solve a Problem

Solve each problem in two ways, using each of the first steps below. Show your solutions.

NOTE Students develop efficiency and flexibility in their computation skills by solving addition problems in more than one way.

Unit 20–24

1. 378 + 381 =

Start by solving 378 + 300.	Start by solving 300 + 300.

2. 566 + 284 =

Start by solving 500 + 200.	Start by solving 284 + 16.

Session 2.4　　Unit 8　35

▲ **Student Activity Book, p. 35**

SESSION FOLLOW-UP

3 Daily Practice and Homework

 Daily Practice: For ongoing review, have students complete *Student Activity Book* page 34.

Homework: On *Student Activity Book* page 35, students practice solving addition problems, given two different starts.

Student Math Handbook: Students and families may use *Student Math Handbook* pages 20–24, 25 and G8 for reference and review. See pages 179–189 in the back of this unit.

Assessment: Addition Strategies

Math Focus Points

◆ Solving addition problems with more than 2 addends

◆ Solving addition problems with 3-digit numbers

Vocabulary

addend

Today's Plan		Materials
DISCUSSION **① Solving Multiple-Addend Problems**	15 MIN CLASS	
ASSESSMENT ACTIVITY **② Addition Strategies**	✔ 20 MIN INDIVIDUALS	• M40*
MATH WORKSHOP **③ Practicing Addition** **3A** Multiple-Addend Problems **3B** More Addition Problems **3C** *Collections Match*	25 MIN	**3A** • *Student Activity Book*, pp. 30–31 **3B** • *Student Activity Book*, p. 32 **3C** • *Student Activity Book*, p. 33 • M31–M38 (from Unit 3 or Session 2.4); M39*
SESSION FOLLOW-UP **④ Daily Practice**		• *Student Activity Book*, p. 37 • *Student Math Handbook*, pp. 20–24, 25

*See *Materials to Prepare*, p. 63.

Ten-Minute Math

Guess My Rule Choose a rule that describes a type of living thing such as "reptiles". Inside a large circle, write the names of several things that fit the rule. As students suggest animals, place them inside or outside the circle. Students deduce what the rule is from the evidence. After the rule has been established, ask students:

• Is the number of animals that fit the rule more or less than half the total? How do you know?

Students discuss what is about half of the total.

15 MIN   CLASS

DISCUSSION

Solving Multiple-Addend Problems

Math Focus Points for Discussion

◆ Solving addition problems with more than 2 addends

Write Problem 3 from *Student Activity Book* page 30 on the board. Students should have completed this problem during the previous Math Workshop.

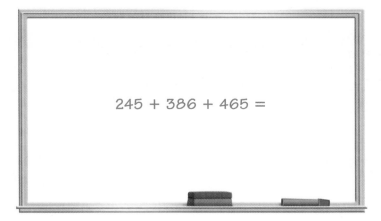

$$245 + 386 + 465 =$$

How did you solve this problem?

Listen for strategies that involve adding the two numbers that end in 5 together because their sum will include a whole 10.

Students might say:

"I saw that both 245 and 465 ended in 5, so I added the 5s together to make 10. 240 and 460 are left to add, and 240 + 460 = 700. Then one more 10 from the two 5s is 710."

Students should understand that they can use familiar strategies to break apart and recombine parts of numbers in problems in which there are more than two addends. They can still break the numbers apart by place value, for instance. For multiple-addend problems, however, it is particularly useful to use strategies that involve looking for combinations that are already familiar, such as multiples of 10 or 100.

Ask students to consider a problem with more than three addends.

What if we had four numbers? How would you figure out the answer to this problem?

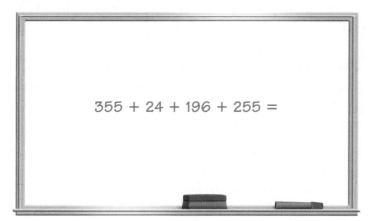

$$355 + 24 + 196 + 255 =$$

Give students a few minutes to work on this problem, and then have students share their starting strategies. This problem includes two different pairs of numbers that add up to a multiple of 10 (355 + 255 and 24 + 196). Students may note one, the other, or both. Elicit examples of different approaches to the problem.

Students might say:

"I added 24 and 196 first. I saw that 196 plus 4 would make 200. That leaves 20 from the 24, which is 220."

"First, I added 55 and 55. That's 110. Then, add on 200 and 300, so it's 610."

Now ask students to consider the question of whether the order matters when there are more than two addends.

You already know that when there are two numbers in an addition problem, you get the same answer no matter in what order you add them. So 3 plus 5 will give you the same answer as 5 plus 3, and 45 plus 33 will give you the same answer as 33 plus 45.

In this problem, it seems that most of you are changing the order of the numbers, too. Some of you started with 196 + 24 and some of you started with 355 + 255. Do you think it's true that the order of the

Professional Development

① Teacher Note: Assessment: Addition Strategies, p. 156

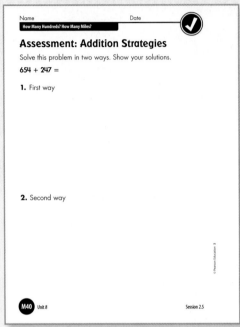

▲ **Resource Masters, M40** PORTFOLIO

numbers still doesn't matter if there are more than two numbers in an addition problem? Would we get the same answer to this problem if I moved the numbers around?

Write the same problem in a different order on the board.

$$196 + 255 + 355 + 24$$

After students discuss this with a partner for a few minutes, collect their responses. Students have already been solving these multiple-addend problems by changing the order of the numbers, but listen for their explanation of *why* this works.

Their responses should include knowing that the numbers represent the same numbers or amounts (of objects, or money, or whatever students might use as a context), no matter in what order they are added, as long as nothing is added or removed.

ASSESSMENT ACTIVITY

② Addition Strategies

20 MIN INDIVIDUALS

This assessment addresses Benchmark 2: Solve 3-digit addition problems, using at least one strategy efficiently. You will have another chance to assesss students on this benchmark in the End-of-Unit Assessment.

Hand out Assessment: Addition Strategies (M40), on which students solve an addition problem in two ways. Let them know that they will be working individually so that you can learn how each of them is solving addition problems.

Today you're going to solve an addition problem in two ways. Begin by using the strategy that is easiest for you and that you understand the best. Then think about how else you could solve the problem, perhaps by using a strategy that you've seen someone else use or that you've been trying out for yourself. Be sure to record your strategies clearly. Anyone looking at your paper should be able to understand both ways that you solved the problem.

Through this assessment, you can see which addition strategies your students are using, and how accurately and efficiently students are using them. At this point in the year, all students should have at least one addition strategy that they can use with fluency. By asking students to solve the problem in more than one way, you can determine whether students are also developing flexibility in their computation.①

MATH WORKSHOP

③ Practicing Addition

 25 MIN

Students continue to work on practicing addition with the Math Workshop activities from the last session.

③A Multiple-Addend Problems

 INDIVIDUALS

For complete details on this activity, see Session 2.4, page 87.

③B More Addition Problems

 INDIVIDUALS

For complete details on this activity, see Session 2.4, page 88.

③C Collections Match

 PAIRS

For complete details on this activity, see Session 2.4, page 89.

Math Workshop offers further practice with addition strategies.

Name _____ Date _____

How Many Hundreds? How Many Miles?

Addition and Subtraction: Related Problems 2 🖊

Daily Practice

NOTE Students use what they know from solving one problem to help them solve related addition and subtraction problems.

20–24, 32–35

1. Solve each set of related problems.

Set 1	Set 2
400 + 200 = _____	500 − 50 = _____
401 + 201 = _____	500 − 60 = _____
399 + 198 = _____	500 − 62 = _____

Set 3			Set 4		
300	298	310	1,000	900	702
300	297	290	− 50	− 50	− 50
+300	+301	+295			

2. Pick one problem set. Explain how you used some of the problems in the set to solve others.

_____

_____

_____

Session 2.5   Unit 8   37

▲ **Student Activity Book, p. 37**

SESSION FOLLOW-UP

④ Daily Practice

 Daily Practice: For reinforcement of this unit's content, have students complete *Student Activity Book* page 37.

 Student Math Handbook: Students and families may use *Student Math Handbook* pages 20–24, 25 for reference and review. See pages 179–189 in the back of this unit.

Mathematical Emphases

Computational Fluency Adding and subtracting accurately and efficiently

Math Focus Points

◆ Solving addition problems with 3-digit numbers

◆ Estimating which of two sums is greater

◆ Using the relationship of numbers in a subtraction expression to multiples of 100 to solve subtraction problems

◆ Knowing and using subtraction problems related to the addition combinations to 10 + 10 (the subtraction facts, e.g., 8 − 5, 13 − 9) with fluency

◆ Solving addition and subtraction problems in the context of money (dollars, cents)

◆ Solving addition problems with more than 2 addends

◆ Determining combinations of addends for a given sum

◆ Solving addition and subtraction problems with more than one step

Whole-Number Operations Describing, analyzing, and comparing strategies for adding and subtracting whole numbers

Math Focus Points

◆ Solving subtraction problems that involve comparison, removal, or finding a missing part

◆ Subtracting 3-digit numbers by using strategies that involve either subtracting one number in parts, adding up, or subtracting back

◆ Representing solutions to subtraction problems with number lines, 1,000 charts, and/or story contexts

◆ Using story contexts and representations to support explanations about how changing a number in a subtraction problem affects the difference (e.g., $200 - 75 = 125$ and $200 - 78 = 122$)

◆ Subtracting by using strategies that involve changing one number to make a problem that is easier to solve

Subtraction

	Student Activity Book	Student Math Handbook	Professional Development: Read Ahead of Time	
SESSION 3.1 p. 102				
Collections Compare Students play a game in which they add 2- and 3-digit numbers and compare the sums, using estimation and computation strategies.	38–40	20–24; G7	• **Teacher Note:** Types of Subtraction Situations, p. 160	
SESSION 3.2 p. 109				
Travel Problems Students find the difference between 3-digit numbers in the context of distances traveled on a fictional journey.	41–44	32–35	• **Teacher Note:** Learning and Assessing Subtraction Facts Related to Addition Combinations to 10 + 10, p. 162	
SESSION 3.3 p. 116				
Assessment: Subtraction Strategies Students solve and write a story about a 3-digit subtraction problem. They discuss their solutions and ways to represent their strategies. They are assessed on their subtraction strategies.	45–47	32–35	• **Teacher Note:** Subtraction Strategies, p. 163; Assessment: Subtraction Strategies, p. 165	
SESSION 3.4 p. 123				
Money Problems and Assessment: Subtraction Facts Students solve subtraction problems that involve spending money and making change. They are assessed on their knowledge of subtraction facts that are related to addition combinations to 10 + 10.	49–53	31, 32–35	• **Teacher Note:** Reasoning and Proof in Mathematics, p. 168	
SESSION 3.5 p. 128				
Subtracting Whole Dollars Students consider how to solve a subtraction problem with money by changing one of the numbers to a whole-dollar amount to create an easier problem.	49–51, 55	32–35		
SESSION 3.6 p. 132				
Strategies for Subtraction Students solve subtraction problems with 3-digit numbers in a variety of contexts. They describe and compare their strategies.	56–59	32–35		

Materials to Gather	Materials to Prepare
• **T101**, *Collections Compare* **Recording Sheet** 🖵 • **T25–T32**, **Collections Cards** (from Unit 3) 🖵 • **M31–M38**, **Collections Cards** (1 set per student; from Unit 3 or Session 2.4)	• **M41**, *Collections Compare* Make copies. (as needed) Play a few rounds ahead of time to familiarize yourself with the mathematics involved in this game. • **M42**, *Collections Compare* **Recording Sheet** Make copies. (1 per student) • **Chart paper** Label a sheet of chart paper with the heading "Which Collections Have More?" and list the paired collections shown on pages 106 and 107.
• **Chart paper** (optional) • **Subtraction Cards** (from Unit 3; 1 set per student) • **Envelopes** (2 per student; as needed) • **Oregon Trail background material** If your students are not familiar with the story of the Oregon Trail, you may want to spend a little time outside math class sharing information about this period of U.S. history.	• **M43**, **Practicing the Subtraction Facts** Make copies. (1 per student) • **M44–M51**, **Subtraction Cards** Make copies and cut apart to replace lost cards. (1 set per student; as needed)
• **M25–M29, 1,000 Charts** (1 per student; from Session 2.2; optional) • **Chart paper** • **M44–M51**, **Subtraction Cards** (1 set per student; from Session 3.2)	• **M52**, **Assessment: Subtraction Strategies** Make copies. (1 per student)
• **Play money** (1 set per student, optional) • **Subtraction Cards** (1 set per student; from Unit 3 or Session 3.2)	• **M53**, **Assessment: Subtraction Facts** Make copies. (1 per student; optional)
• **Play money** (optional) • **Subtraction Cards** (from Unit 3 or Session 3.2) • **Collections Cards** (from Unit 3 or Session 2.4)	• **M42**, *Collections Compare* **Recording Sheet** (from Session 3.1) • **M53**, **Assessment: Subtraction Facts** (1 per student; from Session 3.4; optional)
• **Chart paper** (as needed)	

🖵 Overhead Transparency

Subtraction, *continued*

		Student Activity Book	Student Math Handbook	Professional Development: Read Ahead of Time	
SESSION 3.7	p. 137				
What Combinations Can I Make? Students find different combinations of numbers to make a given sum and solve addition and subtraction story problems with more than one step.		61–66	20–24, 32–35		
SESSION 3.8	p. 142				
Making Combinations Students discuss their strategies for finding combinations of amounts of money with a sum close to $10 and continue to practice addition and subtraction.		61–64, 67	20–24, 32–35		
SESSION 3.9	p. 146				
End-of-Unit Assessment Students solve three problems to assess their strategies for solving addition and subtraction problems with 3-digit numbers.		68–69	20–24, 32–35	• **Teacher Note:** End-of-Unit Assessment, p. 171	

Materials to Gather	Materials to Prepare
• **Play money** (as needed; optional)	• **Chart paper** Label a chart with the heading "$100 for Supplies," and list the items and prices shown on page 138.
• **Chart paper** (optional) • **Play money** (as needed; optional)	
	• **M54–M55, End-of-Unit Assessment** Make copies. (1 set per student)

Collections Compare

Math Focus Points

◆ Solving addition problems with 3-digit numbers

◆ Solving subtraction problems that involve comparison

◆ Estimating which of two sums is greater

Vocabulary

sum
difference

Today's Plan			Materials
ACTIVITY **①** **Introducing** *Collections Compare*	🕐 15 MIN	👥 CLASS	• M41 (as needed) • T25–T32 (from Unit 3) 💾; T101 💾
ACTIVITY **②** **Playing** *Collections Compare*	🕐 30 MIN	👥 PAIRS	• *Student Activity Book,* p. 38 • M42 (as needed)* • M31–M38, Collection Cards (from Session 2.4)
DISCUSSION **③** **Which Collections Have More?**	🕐 15 MIN	👥 CLASS	• Chart: "Which Collections Have More?"*
SESSION FOLLOW-UP **④** **Daily Practice and Homework**			• *Student Activity Book,* pp. 39–40 • *Student Math Handbook,* pp. 20–24; G7

*See *Materials to Prepare,* p. 99.

Ten-Minute Math

Counting Around the Class Ask questions about an imaginary class that was counting by 4s. Ask:

• When the class finished counting, the last number was 80. How many students are in that class?

• What number did the fifth person say?

• What number did the tenth person say?

For each question, collect answers as well as explanations about how students found their answer.

ACTIVITY

1 Introducing *Collections Compare*

15 MIN **CLASS**

Students play *Collections Compare,* a game similar to other *Compare* games they have played in the primary grades. In this version, players each turn over two Collection Cards, add the numbers on their cards, and determine who has the larger sum. Students can read the rules of the game on *Collections Compare* (M41).

Today we're going to play a game called Collections Compare. *Just like other comparing games you've played before, your job is to figure out who has the larger sum.*

To explain how the game is played, play a sample round with the class. Ask for a volunteer to play with you. Each player draws two cards from a transparent deck of Collection Cards (T25–T32) for display on the overhead. (Alternatively, use regular Collection Cards and simply write the numbers from the cards on the board or overhead.) Point out that for this game, it is not necessary for the cards in a pair to be a "match" in terms of type of collection.

Here's a sample round of Collections Compare. *Take a couple of minutes to figure out which of us has the larger sum when we each combine our two cards. You can use any strategy you choose.*

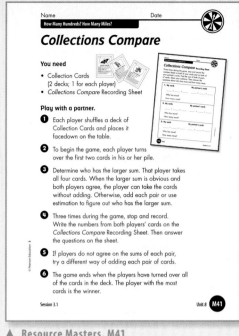

▲ **Resource Masters, M41**

Math Note

❶ Problems About Comparison Students often solve comparison problems by determining either how much more they would need to add to the smaller amount to equal the larger amount or how much they would need to subtract from the larger amount to equal the smaller amount. This is because these strategies are a direct representation of the action of comparing two amounts. However, some students recognize that they can use any subtraction strategy to solve such problems.

Professional Development

❷ Teacher Note: Types of Subtraction Situations, p. 160

Name _____ Date _____

How Many Hundreds? How Many Miles?

Collections Compare Recording Sheet

Three times during the game, stop and record the numbers listed on both of your cards and on both of your partner's cards. Find the sum of both pairs of cards. Show your solutions. Then answer the questions about who has more and how many more.

1. My cards   **My partner's cards**
____ + ____ = ____   ____ + ____ = ____

Who has more?

How many more?

2. My cards   **My partner's cards**
____ + ____ = ____   ____ + ____ = ____

Who has more?

How many more?

3. My cards   **My partner's cards**
____ + ____ = ____   ____ + ____ = ____

Who has more?

How many more?

38 Unit 8   Session 3.1

▲ **Student Activity Book, p. 38; Resource Masters, M42; T101**

Collect two or three examples of students' strategies for determining the larger sum. You will probably find that some students have added the amounts on each pair of cards and that others determined the larger sum without actually adding the amounts.

Students might say:

"Each of you has one card that is almost the same amount, but Kelley's other card is way more than your other card. So Kelley has more."

When you play *Collections Compare,* you will sometimes be able to "just know" which pair of cards has the larger sum. Other times you will need to do the calculation to figure it out.

Let students know that as they play the game, they choose three hands to record on *Student Activity Book* page 38. In addition to calculating the two sums, students are also asked to figure out the difference between the two sums.❶❷

Three times during the game, you'll have one more question to answer: How many more is the larger sum? Let's answer that with this round. How many more are there on Kelley's cards than on mine?

Give students a minute or two to figure this out. Demonstrate how to record their responses on the transparent *Collections Compare* Recording Sheet (T101).

ACTIVITY

② Playing *Collections Compare*

30 MIN   PAIRS

Students play *Collections Compare* in pairs. This game provides practice with addition strategies and gives students a context in which to think about one type of subtraction situation—comparing two quantities.

Remind students to fill in *Student Activity Book* page 38 for three pairs of matches in each game. If students play more than one game, make available copies of *Collections Compare* Recording Sheet (M42).

Collections Compare *offers practice with estimation as well as addition and subtraction.*

ONGOING ASSESSMENT: Observing Students at Work

Students compare two pairs of 2-digit and 3-digit numbers to determine which has the larger sum.

- **Do students use the relative size of the numbers and estimate to determine the larger sum when that is a reasonable approach?** (e.g., "I knew that 296 was almost 300, so I had a total of about 380. My partner's cards were about 210 and about 150. If you add those together, it's 360, so I knew I had more.")

- **Do students add accurately when they need to do so to determine which pair has the larger sum?**

- **Do students have a strategy for finding the difference between the two numbers they are comparing?** Do they add up, subtract back, or subtract one number from the other? Do they carry out their strategies accurately?

Notice which students are using estimation to determine the larger sum, which students need to focus more on their addition strategies, and which students need help with their subtraction strategies for the comparison part of the activity.

Algebra Note

❸ Reasoning About Comparisons When students reason about which group has the most without adding, they may be using one of several general principles. For example, when comparing 840 and 185 with 840 and 118, students might reason, "If two numbers are equal and you add more to one than the other, the sum of the larger number and the original will be greater than the other sum." Written in formal symbols, this idea can be expressed in this way: If $x = y$ and $a > b$, then $x + a > y + b$.

Asking students to explain and represent how they know which sum is larger without adding helps them express and reason about the general case.

DIFFERENTIATION: Supporting the Range of Learners

Intervention Students who need to focus on subtraction with smaller numbers may play the game by turning over only one card each and then comparing those two amounts. In this case, these students are focusing only on the comparison aspect of the activity and are not getting addition practice as well.

DISCUSSION

15 MIN CLASS

③ Which Collections Have More?

Math Focus Points for Discussion

◆ Estimating which of two sums is greater

After students have played *Collections Compare,* bring them together to discuss some of the comparison problems they encountered and the different strategies they used.❸

Call attention to the first set on the chart you prepared.

> ### Which Collections Have More?
>
> #### Set 1
>
> Pilar: 253 puzzles and
>   58 stacking dolls
>
> Gil: 148 board games and
>   143 Canadian stamps

This is a set of four cards that you might have turned over when you played *Collections Compare.* What strategies could you use to decide who has more? Do some strategies work better for some problems than others do?

A good strategy for this problem is estimating the total number of objects in each collection and comparing the totals. Listen for students' responses that point out the following logic:

- Both collections are going to be close to 300 because each sum includes two 100s and about two 50s left over.

- In Pilar's collection, both 53 and 58 are more than 50, so the sum is more than 100 and Pilar has *more than 300* in her combined collections.

- In Gil's collection, both 48 and 43 are less than 50, so that sum is less than 100 and Gil has *fewer than 300* in his combined collections.

Next, call attention to the collections in Set 2.

Set 2

Murphy: 61 stacking dolls and
        209 antique children's books

Nancy: 58 snakes and
       184 alphabet books

A strategy that works well for this problem is comparing the sizes of the individual collections. Again, listen for students' responses that have the following logic to discuss the strategy in general.

- Murphy's 61 stacking dolls are more than Nancy's 58 snakes.

- Murphy's 209 antique children's books are more than Nancy's 184 alphabet books.

- Because both of Murphy's collections are bigger than Nancy's, Murphy has more in his combined collection.

Notice that a crucial part of this strategy is choosing the appropriate pairs to compare. The strategy will not work if a student compares 61 with 184 and 58 with 209.

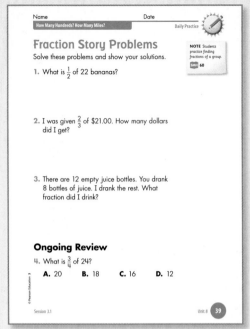

▲ Student Activity Book, p. 39

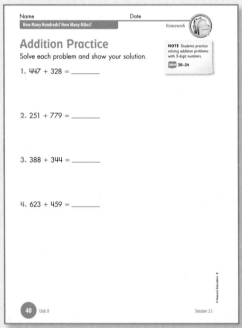

▲ Student Activity Book, p. 40

These two strategies will work well for many problems. You may want to challenge the class with the following problem, which requires a more complicated strategy:

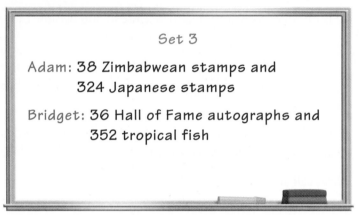

> **Set 3**
>
> Adam: 38 Zimbabwean stamps and
> 324 Japanese stamps
>
> Bridget: 36 Hall of Fame autographs and
> 352 tropical fish

One way to think about this problem is to notice that Adam has two more Zimbabwean stamps than Bridget has autographs, but he has about 30 fewer Japanese stamps than Bridget's tropical fish. Therefore, although Adam has a little more than Bridget in comparing two of the collections, he has many fewer when the other two collections are compared, and his total collection is smaller than Bridget's.

SESSION FOLLOW-UP
Daily Practice and Homework

Daily Practice: For ongoing review, have students complete *Student Activity Book* page 39.

Homework: On *Student Activity Book* page 40, students solve addition problems with 3-digit numbers.

Student Math Handbook: Students and families may use *Student Math Handbook* pages 20–24 and G7 for reference and review. See pages 179–189 in the back of this unit.

Travel Problems

Math Focus Points

◆ Solving subtraction problems that involve finding a missing part

◆ Using the relationship of numbers in a subtraction expression to multiples of 100 to solve subtraction problems

Vocabulary

landmark

Today's Plan		Materials
ACTIVITY **① Travel Problems** 45 MIN　PAIRS　CLASS		• *Student Activity Book,* pp. 41–42 • Oregon Trail background material
DISCUSSION **② Strategies for Finding the Distance** 15 MIN　CLASS		• *Student Activity Book,* p. 41 • Chart paper (optional)
SESSION FOLLOW-UP **③ Daily Practice and Homework**		• *Student Activity Book,* pp. 43–44 • M43*; M44–M51 (or student sets from Unit 3)* • *Student Math Handbook,* pp. 32–35

*See *Materials to Prepare,* p. 99.

Ten-Minute Math

Counting Around the Class Ask students questions about an imaginary group of students counting by 6s. Ask:

• When the group finished counting, the last number was 72. How many students are in that group?

• What number did the third person say?

• What number did the fifth person say?

For each question, collect answers as well as explanations about how students found their answers.

Teaching Note

❶ **The Oregon Trail** From 1843 to 1869, the route known as the Oregon Trail was the major corridor for settlers, many of them families with children, to travel into the western part of the United States. It involved almost 2,000 miles of travel by foot, horse, and covered wagon. Travelers had to cross several major rivers as well as the Rocky Mountains. It was a long, hard, and dangerous journey, taking 4 to 6 months. Note that the maps students are using show the boundaries of current states for reference, although in 1847, this area was all territories and open land. Your students may want to find out more about the Oregon Trail either online or in your school library.

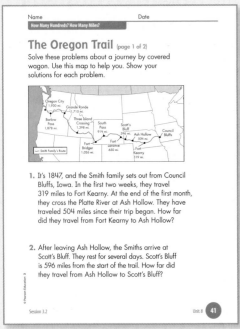

▲ Student Activity Book, p. 41

ACTIVITY

❶ Travel Problems

45 MIN PAIRS CLASS

In this session, students solve problems about finding distances between places along the historic Oregon Trail.❶ Begin this session by reading aloud the first problem on *Student Activity Book* page 41 and examining the map with the class.

These problems are all about a pioneer family, the Smiths, who traveled out west in their covered wagon. The map on this page shows their route along the Oregon Trail, and it shows some of the places where the Smith family stopped along the trail. The numbers on the map tell how many miles they had traveled from the beginning of their trip each time they stopped.

Make sure that students understand that each place is labeled with the number of miles that represents its distance from the start of the trail. This is the important information that they will have to keep track of in order to solve the problems. As needed, point out that these mileage designations differ from the "mileage between points" that students may have seen on road maps.

The first problem asks how far the Smiths traveled from Fort Kearny to Ash Hollow. How can you use this map to help you find out?

Give students a few minutes to discuss the map.

Without finding the exact answer, about how many miles do you think it was from Fort Kearny to Ash Hollow? Did the family travel more or less than 100 miles?

Collect estimates for the distance between 319 miles and 504 miles. Some students may offer a visual image of the "space" between the two points on the map in relation to a number line.

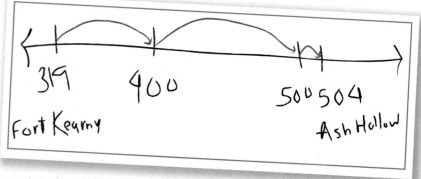

Sample Student Work

Students might say:

"It's like you've got this much from 319 to 400, then there's 400 to 500, and a little more to 504. That's definitely more than a hundred miles, maybe even close to 200."

Students now work on the problems on *Student Activity Book* pages 41–42 in pairs. Encourage them to help each other read the problems, read the map, and discuss how they "see" what's happening as the Smith family's travels continue. All students should complete Problems 1–4. Problems 5–8 take the numbers over 1,000 and are intended only for those students ready for this challenge.

ONGOING ASSESSMENT: Observing Students at Work

Students solve subtraction problems that involve finding the distance in miles between one place and another.

- **What strategies do students use to solve these problems?** Do they add up from one number to another or subtract back, stopping off at multiples of 10 or 100 along the way? Do they subtract the smaller number from the larger by breaking the numbers apart in some way?

- **Are students using the strategies they choose efficiently, using larger chunks of the numbers rather than smaller?**

- **Are students' computations accurate?**

DIFFERENTIATION: Supporting the Range of Learners

Intervention Some students may need help finding the mathematical information embedded in the story. Ask them to picture what is happening as the family travels from one place to another, and help them pull out the numbers they need to work with for each problem.

Extension Students who quickly solve Problems 1–4 should have time to spend on the problems with larger numbers (Problems 5–8).

ELL You might group English Language Learners and work with them on this activity instead of having them work independently in pairs. To guide students through the travel problems, read aloud one sentence at a time. Ask students to paraphrase, using the map. If needed, ask them to sketch pictures to show how they "see" what is happening as the Smith family travels.

Math Note

② Finding a Missing Part Students are familiar with this type of subtraction problem, particularly in the context of traveling, from their work in Unit 3, *Collections and Travel Stories.* In these problems, they must find the difference between the whole amount (the distance traveled so far) and one part of that amount (the distance traveled to a previous stop). Having visual images they can refer to, such as a map or number line, helps students keep track of what is happening mathematically in these problems.

The Oregon Trail (page 2 of 2)

3. When the family arrives at Fort Laramie, they are 650 miles from the start of the trail. How far did they travel from Scott's Bluff to Fort Laramie?

4. The Smiths cross the Continental Divide at South Pass, which is 914 miles from the start of the trail. How far is Fort Laramie from South Pass?

5. Fort Bridger is 1,026 miles from the start of the Smiths' trip. When they reach Three Island Crossing, they are 1,398 miles from their start. How far is it from Fort Bridger to Three Island Crossing?

6. Before reaching Barlow Pass, the family rests at Grande Ronde. They are 1,710 miles from the beginning of the trail. How far did they travel from Three Island Crossing to Grande Ronde?

7. At Barlow Pass, the Smiths' horses are tired. They have walked 1,878 miles on this trip! How far is it from Grande Ronde to Barlow Pass?

8. Finally, the Smiths arrive in Oregon City. They have traveled 1,930 miles altogether. How many miles was the last leg of their journey, from the Barlow Pass to Oregon City?

▲ Student Activity Book, p. 42

DISCUSSION

2 Strategies for Finding the Distance

15 MIN **CLASS**

Math Focus Points for Discussion

◆ Using the relationship of numbers in a subtraction expression to multiples of 100 to solve subtraction problems

Bring the class together to discuss Problem 3 on *Student Activity Book* page 42, which asks for the distance from Scott's Bluff (596 miles from the start) to Fort Laramie (650 miles from the start). Ask several students to share their strategies, and record these on the board or chart paper. Because of the distance context, it is likely that many students pictured the action of this problem as adding up from 596 to 650 or perhaps as subtracting back from 650 to 596. As students share their strategies, listen for the ways that they used 600 as a landmark.

Students might say:

"I started at 596, and I knew I only had to go 4 miles to get to 600. Then there's 50 more, so that's 54 altogether."

Sample Student Work

With students' help, draw a number line on the board to show this strategy.

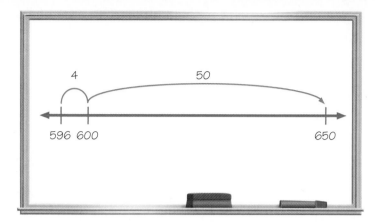

Now ask students to consider another distance that they have not been asked to figure out in the problems—the distance between Scott's Bluff (at mile 596) and South Pass (at mile 914). Draw a new number line for this.

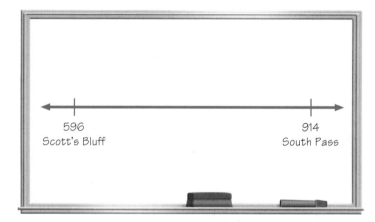

What if we wanted to find the distance between these two points on the Oregon Trail, Scott's Bluff and South Pass? What other numbers should we put on this number line to help us?

Encourage students to continue thinking about how multiples of 100 can serve as landmarks as they visualize the difference between these two numbers on the number line.

In the first problem, and in previous discussions, students worked with situations in which there was only one multiple of 100 between two numbers, such as 596 and 650. As the difference between the numbers increases and the numbers are therefore farther apart on the number line, students consider a wider span that includes several multiples of 100 and figure out how to include these in their solutions. Students may want to label every multiple of 100 in between (600, 700, 800, and 900). If that is the case, ask whether they can combine those distances to take a larger and more efficient jump.

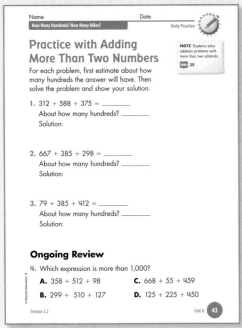

▲ Student Activity Book, p. 43

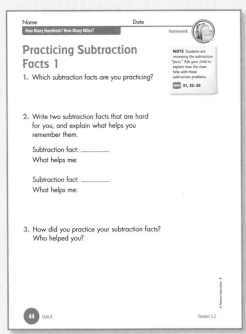

▲ Student Activity Book, p. 44

As students offer their ideas, draw something like this on the number line:

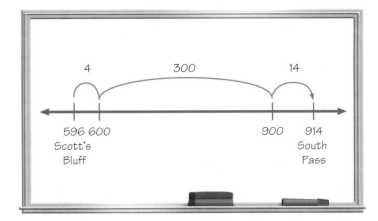

Ask students to help you write this strategy with equations.

$$596 + 4 = 600$$

$$600 + 300 = 900$$

$$900 + 14 = 914$$

$$4 + 300 + 14 = 318$$

What would this look like if we were subtracting back from 914 to 596?

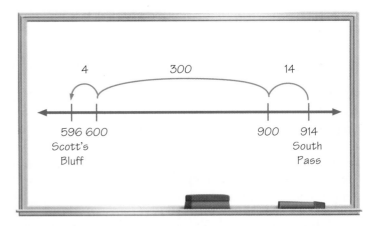

Students should notice that this strategy uses the same chunks of numbers.

$$914 - 14 = 900$$

$$900 - 300 = 600$$

$$600 - 4 = 596$$

$$14 + 300 + 4 = 318$$

Finish this discussion by reminding students that adding up or subtracting back in this particular way, by using the multiples of 100 in between as landmarks, is only one kind of strategy for finding the difference between two numbers. They will be practicing and discussing other strategies for subtraction in the next few sessions.

❸ **Teacher Note:** Learning and Assessing Subtraction Facts Related to Addition Combinations to 10 + 10, p. 162

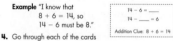

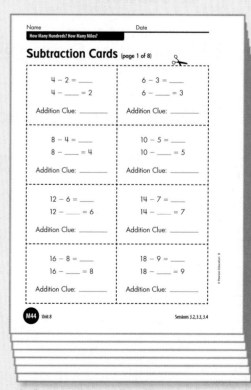

SESSION FOLLOW-UP

③ Daily Practice and Homework

Daily Practice: For reinforcement of this unit's content, have students complete *Student Activity Book* page 43.

Homework: Students continue the work they have been doing in Grade 3 on becoming fluent with subtraction facts. They will need their sets of Subtraction Cards from Unit 3. Also send home Practicing the Subtraction Facts (M43) and Subtraction Cards (M44–M51). On *Student Activity Book* page 44, students record how they worked with a friend or family member on particular subtraction facts. They will be assessed on the subtraction facts in Session 4 of this Investigation.❸

Student Math Handbook: Students and families may use *Student Math Handbook* pages 32–35 for reference and review. See pages 179–189 in the back of this unit.

▲ **Resource Masters, M43**

▲ **Resource Masters, M44–M51**

Assessment: Subtraction Strategies

Math Focus Points

◆ Subtracting 3-digit numbers by using strategies that involve either subtracting one number in parts, adding up, or subtracting back

◆ Solving subtraction problems that involve comparison, removal, or finding a missing part

◆ Representing solutions to subtraction problems with number lines, 1,000 charts, and/or story contexts

Today's Plan		Materials
① ACTIVITY Solving a Subtraction Problem	🕐 20 MIN 👤 INDIVIDUALS	• *Student Activity Book,* p. 45 • 1,000 Charts (from Unit 3, optional)
② DISCUSSION Breaking Numbers Apart to Subtract	🕐 20 MIN 👥 CLASS	• Chart paper
③ ASSESSMENT ACTIVITY Subtraction Strategies	✓ 🕐 20 MIN 👤 INDIVIDUALS	• M52*
④ SESSION FOLLOW-UP Daily Practice and Homework		• *Student Activity Book,* pp. 46–47 • Subtraction Cards (from Unit 3) • *Student Math Handbook,* pp. 32–35

*See *Materials to Prepare,* p. 99.

Ten-Minute Math

Counting Around the Class Ask students questions about an imaginary group of students that was counting by 20s. Ask:

· When the group finished counting, the last number was 300. How many students were in that group?

Encourage students to consider what they know about how many 20s there are in 100. Ask:

· What number did the fifth person say?

· What number did the 10th person say?

For each question, collect answers as well as explanations about how students found their answers.

ACTIVITY
Solving a Subtraction Problem

20 MIN **INDIVIDUALS**

Begin this session by reminding students of the work they did with different types of subtraction problems in Unit 3, *Collections and Travel Stories.*

Do you remember when we talked about different kinds of subtraction story problems? We saw that they can be about removing or taking something away, about comparing two things, or about finding the missing part of a whole.

Today you're going to have a subtraction problem to write a story about and then solve. Think about what kind of story will help you visualize the difference between these two numbers in the problem. You may also use your 1,000 chart or a number line if that will help you.

Give students about 15–20 minutes to work on *Student Activity Book* page 45. Take this opportunity to observe the strategies students are using at this point in Grade 3. They should be using strategies that involve breaking the numbers apart in some way, either subtracting one number in parts or adding up or subtracting back in parts to find the difference between the two numbers. ❶ ❷

ONGOING ASSESSMENT: Observing Students at Work

Students write a story problem that represents a given subtraction expression and solve the problem.

- **Do students write a story that involves a subtraction situation, such as "taking away" (or removing) 168 of something from a starting amount of 352?** Do some students write stories that involve other kinds of subtraction situations, such as finding a missing part or comparing the two amounts?

- **Do students have a strategy for solving a subtraction problem with numbers of this size?** How do they break the numbers apart? Do they use multiples of 10 and 100 as landmarks, or stopping-off places, as they either add up or subtract?

- **Do students use representations (1,000 chart, number line) to solve the problem?**

Math Note

❶ **The U.S. Standard Algorithm** Some students in your class may be familiar with the U.S. standard algorithm for subtraction, sometimes called "borrowing" or regrouping. Like the "carrying" or regrouping algorithm for addition, the very thing that makes it efficient—its compactness of notation—also obscures the place value of the numbers and the logic of the steps of the procedure. Too often, students learn to operate with single digits in this algorithm and lose their sense of the meaning of the numbers and of the steps they are taking. Students who can explain to you the logic of each step and the meaning of its shorthand notation can certainly continue using this procedure. They should also learn other strategies in order to expand their understanding of the operation of subtraction. Students will study this algorithm in Grade 5 *after* they have developed efficient and accurate subtraction strategies based on their understanding of the operation of subtraction and the base-ten number system.

Professional Development

❷ **Teacher Note:** Subtraction Strategies, p. 163

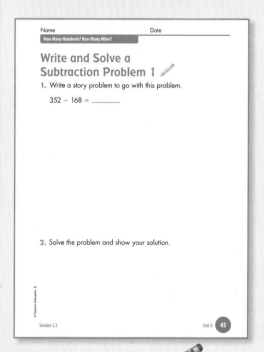

Name _____ Date _____
How Many Hundreds? How Many Miles?

Write and Solve a Subtraction Problem 1

1. Write a story problem to go with this problem.

   $352 - 168 =$ _____

2. Solve the problem and show your solution.

Session 3.3 — Unit 8 **45**

▲ Student Activity Book, p. 45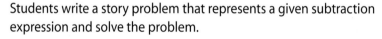

DIFFERENTIATION: Supporting the Range of Learners

 Intervention If some students are unsure how to begin, ask questions such as these:

- Can you break 168 apart in some way so that it will be easier to subtract?

- How can you use a number line or 1,000 chart to show what happens when you subtract 168 from 352? Can you use either of those to show the difference between the two numbers?

- Are there any landmark numbers that might help you here?

Suggesting a number line might help a student who is unsure how to begin to solve a subtraction problem.

20 MIN   CLASS

DISCUSSION

2 Breaking Apart Numbers to Subtract

Math Focus Points for Discussion

◆ Subtracting 3-digit numbers by using strategies that involve either subtracting one number in parts, adding up, or subtracting back

◆ Representing solutions to subtraction problems with number lines, 1,000 charts, and/or story contexts

Bring the class together and begin this discussion by collecting several students' story problems. Write a few of these on chart paper. It is likely that many students will offer problems in which something is being "taken away," which is how students often visualize the type of subtraction problem that we call *removal*. Be sure to include examples of each of the other subtraction problem types as well.❸

Adam's problem

The farmer grew 352 pumpkins. He sold 168 of them. How many did he have left? (taking away)

Bridget's problem

I have 352 bottle caps in my collection. My friend has 168 in her collection. How many more bottle caps do I have than my friend? (comparing)

Gil's problem

There are 352 kids in our school. 168 of them are girls. How many are boys? (finding the missing part)

If no students offer comparison or missing part problems, provide your own examples and ask students how subtraction can be used in these problems.

After you have collected several story problems, ask students to share how they solved the problem and any representations they may have used. In this first of several discussions about subtraction strategies, listen for ways that students broke the numbers apart as they solved the problem. Ask questions such as the following. As students respond, model how to notate the steps they used in each of their strategies.

- [Denzel], when you drew your number line, how did you break the 168 up so that you could subtract it from 352? How much more did you have to subtract after you first subtracted 100? What numbers did you land on as you were making jumps on your number line?

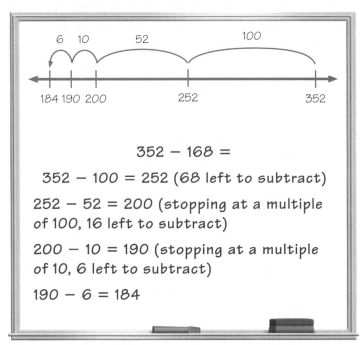

352 − 168 =

352 − 100 = 252 (68 left to subtract)

252 − 52 = 200 (stopping at a multiple of 100, 16 left to subtract)

200 − 10 = 190 (stopping at a multiple of 10, 6 left to subtract)

190 − 6 = 184

- [Zhang], you used a 1,000 chart to find how far it was from 168 to 352, how did you break up that distance? What numbers did you stop off at along the way?

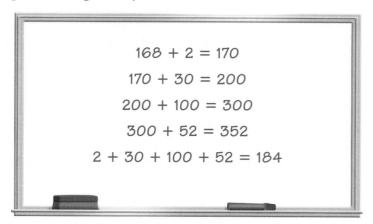

$$168 + 2 = 170$$
$$170 + 30 = 200$$
$$200 + 100 = 300$$
$$300 + 52 = 352$$
$$2 + 30 + 100 + 52 = 184$$

- [Gina], it looks like you broke 168 apart, and first you subtracted 100 from 352, then 60, then 8. Why did you choose those numbers to work with?

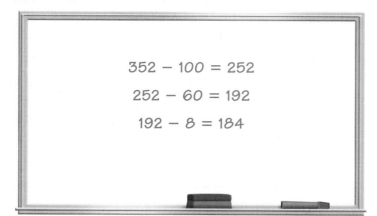

$$352 - 100 = 252$$
$$252 - 60 = 192$$
$$192 - 8 = 184$$

Limit this discussion to about 20 minutes. Over the next few sessions, students will continue to share and discuss their subtraction strategies.

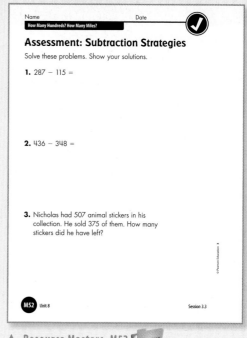

Name _____ Date _____

How Many Hundreds? How Many Miles?

Assessment: Subtraction Strategies

Solve these problems. Show your solutions.

1. $287 - 115 =$

2. $436 - 348 =$

3. Nicholas had 507 animal stickers in his collection. He sold 375 of them. How many stickers did he have left?

M52 Unit 8   Session 3.3

▲ **Resource Masters, M52** PORTFOLIO

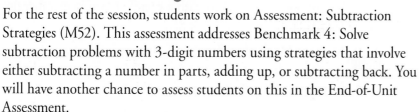

ASSESSMENT ACTIVITY

3 Subtraction Strategies

20 MIN INDIVIDUALS

For the rest of the session, students work on Assessment: Subtraction Strategies (M52). This assessment addresses Benchmark 4: Solve subtraction problems with 3-digit numbers using strategies that involve either subtracting a number in parts, adding up, or subtracting back. You will have another chance to assess students on this in the End-of-Unit Assessment.

Professional Development

 Teacher Note: Assessment: Subtraction Strategies, p. 165

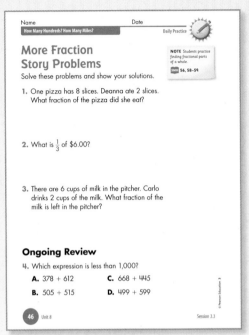

▲ Student Activity Book, p. 46

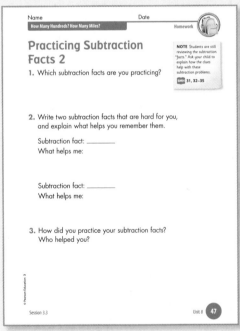

▲ Student Activity Book, p. 47

Students may solve these problems by using any of the strategies that came up in the discussion. Let them know that they may continue to use whatever representations help them.

As you're solving these problems, think about how you can show your solution clearly so that anyone who reads this can follow your thinking.

This assessment provides a way for you to determine which subtraction strategies students are using at this point and how accurately and efficiently they are using them. Your observations will specifically focus on Problem 2 ($436 - 348 = ?$), but consider the range of strategies that students use on all three problems to get a full picture of students' fluency with subtracting 3-digit numbers.

ONGOING ASSESSMENT: Observing Students at Work

Students solve subtraction problems with 3-digit numbers.

- **Do students break the numbers apart in order to make the problems easier to solve?** What size "chunks" of the numbers do they use? Do they add up or subtract multiples of 10 and 100 rather than counting by 10 or 100?

- **Do some students' strategies include using 100 as a "stopping-off" place?** For example, do they solve $507 - 375$ by adding up from 375 to 400 and then adding 107 more or by subtracting 7 from 507 and then 125 more to get to 375?

SESSION FOLLOW-UP

 Daily Practice and Homework

 Daily Practice: For ongoing review, have students complete *Student Activity Book* page 46.

Homework: Students continue their work on becoming fluent with subtraction facts. They will need their sets of Subtraction Cards from Unit 3. On *Student Activity Book* page 47, students record how they worked with a friend or family member on particular facts.

Student Math Handbook: Students and families may use *Student Math Handbook* pages 32–35 for reference and review. See pages 179–189 in the back of this unit.

Money Problems and Assessment: Subtraction Facts

Math Focus Points

◆ Solving subtraction problems that involve comparison, removal, or finding a missing part

◆ Knowing and using subtraction problems related to the addition combinations to $10 + 10$ (the subtraction facts, e.g., $8 - 5$, $13 - 9$) with fluency

◆ Using story contexts and representations to support explanations about how changing a number in a subtraction problem affects the difference (e.g., $200 - 75 = 125$ and $200 - 78 = 122$)

Today's Plan		Materials
① DISCUSSION **How Much Change?**	15 MIN CLASS	• Play money (optional)
② MATH WORKSHOP **Subtraction Problems About Money** **2A** How Much Change? **2B** Earning and Spending **2C** Assessment: Subtraction Facts	45 MIN	**2A** • *Student Activity Book,* pp. 49–50 • Play money (optional) **2B** • *Student Activity Book,* p. 51 • Play money (optional) **2C** • M53 (optional)* • Subtraction Cards (from Unit 3)
③ SESSION FOLLOW-UP **Daily Practice and Homework**		• *Student Activity Book,* pp. 52–53 • *Student Math Handbook,* pp. 31, 32–35

*See *Materials to Prepare,* p. 99.

Ten-Minute Math

Counting Around the Class   Ask students questions about an imaginary group of students that was counting by 25s:

• When the group finished counting, the last number was 300. How many students are in that group?

Encourage students to consider what they know about how many 25s there are in 100. Ask:

• What number did the eighth person say?

• What number did the 10th person say?

For each question, collect answers as well as explanations about how students found their answer.

Math Note

① Do I Add or Subtract? Changing the numbers in a subtraction problem to make a problem that is easier to solve is a useful strategy that depends on knowing how to adjust the difference for the change. This is often confusing to third graders, as well as to many adults. Changing 50 − 29 to 50 − 30 has the effect of "subtracting too much." Having visual images of the operation, which includes being able to tell a story, helps students make sense of this (e.g., "I have 50 apples and I need to give away 29 but instead I give away 30, and that was too many, so I have to take one back"). Third graders are not expected to master this strategy, but they should have the chance to consider it when the numbers make it an efficient possibility. They will study this strategy further in Grade 4. See **Algebra Connections in This Unit,** page 16.

DISCUSSION

① How Much Change?

15 MIN   CLASS

Math Focus Points for Discussion

◆ Using story contexts and representations to support explanations about how changing a number in a subtraction problem affects the difference (e.g., 200 − 75 = 125 and 200 − 78 = 122)

Present students with the following money problem:

Suppose that you go to the grocery store with a 5-dollar bill in your pocket. You buy a couple of things, and the total comes to $2.95, so you give the cashier your 5 dollars. How much change should you get back? Talk about this with your partner for a minute.

Write the equation $5.00 − $2.95 = _____ on the board or overhead. Have sets of play money available for students to use to act out the problem if they wish. When most students have come up with an answer, collect their solutions.

Students might say:

"I've seen some store clerks do this—they count from how much it costs when they hand you back the change. So from $2.95, they give you a nickel and say 3 dollars, then 4 dollars, then 5 dollars. That's 2 dollars and a nickel—2 dollars and 5 cents. It's like adding up."

"If you take 2 dollars away from 5 dollars, it's 3 dollars. Then 95 cents from that leaves 2 dollars and 5 cents."

Listen for any solutions that involve thinking of $2.95 as close to $3; if none come up, suggest this yourself. ①

What if we thought of the problem as 5 dollars minus 3 dollars because 3 dollars is so close to $2.95? Would that be an easy problem to solve? What would we have to do to make it come out as the answer to $5.00 − $2.95? Would the answer to $5.00 − $3.00 be more or less than the answer to $5.00 − $2.95? Why do you think so?

This discussion continues work on the ideas that students considered in Session 1.4. Students may be able to draw on the representations and arguments they made in that session. Let them puzzle about this for a few minutes, using the play money or any other representations that might help them. Then ask students to share their thinking. ❷

Let students know that they will solve more problems about spending money and getting change in Math Workshop.

Students use play money to model a strategy for making change.

MATH WORKSHOP

⏱ 45 MIN

❷ Subtraction Problems About Money

In this Math Workshop, students work on two activities that involve subtraction in the context of money. For both of these, they may work either with a partner or individually. They may use play money, particularly for the problems about getting change on *Student Activity Book* pages 49–50.

Also during Math Workshop in this and the next session, you will meet individually with students to assess their knowledge of subtraction facts.

❷A How Much Change?

INDIVIDUALS   PAIRS

Students determine the amount of change that is given from different whole-dollar amounts to answer the questions on *Student Activity Book* pages 49–50. Although these numbers are given as amounts of money, the problems themselves are similar to others that involve subtracting from multiples of 100, such as the paper clip problems. As you observe students working, notice whether they are using the solutions from earlier problems to solve subsequent problems.

Professional Development

❷ **Teacher Note:** Reasoning and Proof in Mathematics, p. 168

Name _____ Date _____

How Many Hundreds? How Many Miles?

How Much Change? (page 1 of 2)

Answer these questions. You may use play money to help you.

1. At the grocery store, you spend $1.49.
   a. How much change will you get if you pay with two one-dollar bills ($2.00)? _____

   b. How much change will you get if you pay with a five-dollar bill ($5.00)? _____

   c. How much change will you get if you pay with a ten-dollar bill ($10.00)? _____

2. At the trading card store, you spend $3.78.
   a. How much change will you get if you pay with four one-dollar bills ($4.00)? _____

   b. How much change will you get if you pay with a five-dollar bill ($5.00)? _____

   c. How much change will you get if you pay with a ten-dollar bill ($10.00)? _____

Sessions 3.4, 3.5   Unit 8   **49**

▲ **Student Activity Book, p. 49**

Name _____ Date _____

How Many Hundreds? How Many Miles?

How Much Change? (page 2 of 2)

3. At the snack bar, you spend $4.25.
   a. How much change will you get if you pay with a five-dollar bill ($5.00)? _____

   b. How much change will you get if you pay with a ten-dollar bill ($10.00)? _____

   c. How much change will you get if you pay with a twenty-dollar bill ($20.00)? _____

50   Unit 8   Sessions 3.4, 3.5

▲ **Student Activity Book, p. 50**

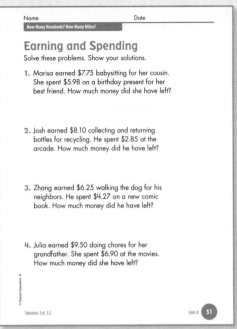

▲ Student Activity Book, p. 51

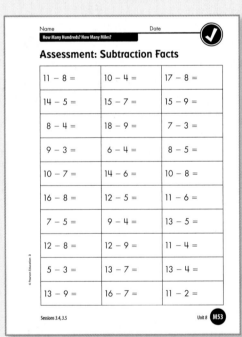

▲ Resource Masters, M53

ONGOING ASSESSMENT: Observing Students at Work

Students solve subtraction problems involving the change given from whole-dollar amounts.

- **What subtraction strategies do students use to determine the amount of change—subtracting the amount paid in parts, adding up from the amount paid to the whole-dollar amount, or other strategies?**

- **Do students use the solutions from earlier problems to solve subsequent problems?** For example, do they see that if $2.00 − $1.49 is $0.51, then $5.00 − $1.49 is 3 dollars more than 51 cents?

- **Are students' computations accurate?**

2B Earning and Spending

INDIVIDUALS PAIRS

Students work on *Student Activity Book* page 51. They should solve at least Problems 1 and 2 during this session.

In these story problems, students subtract from amounts of money that are *not* whole-dollar amounts. However, in most of these problems, the numbers are such that students may change one to a whole-dollar amount to make an easier problem.

ONGOING ASSESSMENT: Observing Students at Work

Students solve story problems about subtracting amounts of money.

- **What subtraction strategies do students use to solve these problems?** Do they subtract the amount spent in parts? Do they find the difference between the two amounts by either adding up or subtracting back?

- **Do students change any amounts to a whole-dollar amount to make an easier problem to solve?** Are they able to adjust for the change accurately?

Encourage students to consider how changing one of the numbers to a whole-dollar amount might make the problem easier to solve. Ask questions such as the following:

- If you changed $5.98 to $6.00, would your answer be more or less than the answer to $7.75 − $5.98?

- If you changed $2.85 to $3.00, how much more have you subtracted? What would you have to do to make the answer come out right?

②C Assessment: Subtraction Facts

INDIVIDUALS

During the Math Workshop in this session and the next, assess students' knowledge of the subtraction facts in one of two ways. Depending on the needs and the size of your class, you might spend a couple of minutes with each student, going through the Subtraction Cards with the addition clues covered. Any problems that students have to stop and figure out are the problems they should continue to work on, either outside math class, when they finish other math activities, or for homework. Plan to assess these students again when you think they are ready.

Alternately, you might have students complete Assessment: Subtraction Facts (M53). To demonstrate fluency, students should be able to complete the 30 problems in about two minutes without looking at the addition clues on their Subtraction Cards.

In either form, this assessment activity addresses Benchmark 3: Demonstrate fluency with subtractions problems related to the addition combinations to 10 + 10 (the subtraction facts).

ONGOING ASSESSMENT: Observing Students at Work

Students solve subtraction problems that are related to the addition combinations to 10 + 10.

- **Can students accurately and quickly solve these problems mentally?**

SESSION FOLLOW-UP

③ Daily Practice and Homework

Daily Practice: For reinforcement of this unit's content, have students complete *Student Activity Book* page 52.

Homework: On *Student Activity Book* page 53, students solve sets of problems with 3-digit numbers. As with other related problem sets, remind students to use the answers to earlier problems to help them with the next problems as they move through the set.

Student Math Handbook: Students and families may use *Student Math Handbook* pages 31, 32–35 for reference and review. See pages 179–189 in the back of this unit.

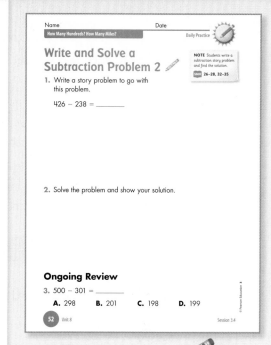

▲ Student Activity Book, p. 52

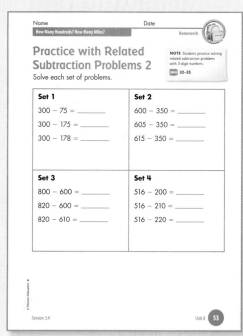

▲ Student Activity Book, p. 53

Subtracting Whole Dollars

Math Focus Points

◆ Subtracting by using strategies that involve changing one number to make a problem that is easier to solve

◆ Solving subtraction problems that involve comparison, removal, or finding a missing part

◆ Knowing and using subtraction problems related to the addition combinations to 10 + 10 (the subtraction facts, e.g., 8 − 5, 13 − 9)

◆ Solving addition and subtraction problems in the context of money (dollars, cents)

Today's Plan		Materials
① DISCUSSION **Subtracting Whole Dollars**	20 MIN CLASS	
② MATH WORKSHOP **Subtraction Problems About Money** **②A** How Much Change? **②B** Earning and Spending **②C** Assessment: Subtraction Facts **②D** *Collections Compare*	40 MIN	**②A** • *Student Activity Book*, pp. 49–50 • Play money (optional) **②B** • *Student Activity Book*, p. 51 • Play money (optional) **②C** • M53 (optional)* • Subtraction Cards (from Unit 3 or Session 3.2) **②D** • M42 (as needed)* • Collections Cards (from Unit 3 or Session 2.4)
③ SESSION FOLLOW-UP **Daily Practice**		• *Student Activity Book*, p. 55 • *Student Math Handbook*, pp. 32–35

*See *Materials to Prepare,* p. 99.

Ten-Minute Math

Guess My Rule Choose a rule that describes something students are wearing such as "wearing jewelry". Select several students who fit the rule to stand in front of the class. Students guess who else fits the rule and who does not, and deduce what the rule is from the evidence. After the rule has been established, ask students:

• Is the number of students who fit the rule more or less than one third of the class? How do you know?

Students discuss what is about one third of the class.

DISCUSSION

① Subtracting Whole Dollars

20 MIN   CLASS

Math Focus Points for Discussion

◆ Subtracting by using strategies that involve changing one number to make a problem that is easier to solve

Show the following set of problems and ask students to solve them:

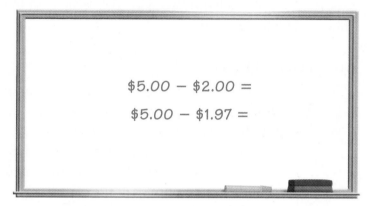

$$\$5.00 - \$2.00 =$$
$$\$5.00 - \$1.97 =$$

How does knowing the answer to $\$5.00 - \$2.00$ help you when the number being subtracted is close to a whole-dollar amount, as in $\$5.00 - \$1.97$? Will the answer to the second problem be more than or less than the first one? How do you know?

In this discussion, listen for students' understanding that in subtraction, the more you take away, the less you have left, and therefore, the reverse is true: if you take away less, you have more left. Ask students to think of ways to visualize this idea, either with a representation or with a story. ❶ ❷

Could someone show us these two subtraction situations on a number line? How would they look different? ❸

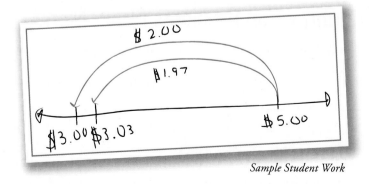

Sample Student Work

Algebra Note

❶ **Using Representations as a Tool for Reasoning** As students share their representations (story contexts, number lines, or other visual models), ask questions to help them make connections among the various representations and to articulate the more general principle involved. "How is the situation seen in the number line model? In the story context? How can you use these same representations to show how $\$5.00 - \$4.00$ helps you solve $\$5.00 - \$3.88$? Can you explain what is happening in these problems without using specific numbers?"

Differentiation

❷ **English Language Learners** You can help English Language Learners prepare for this discussion by giving them similar problems (about subtracting whole dollars) and questions to consider ahead of time. Students can practice their responses with you in a small group. You can then determine what support they might need to explain how they visualize their ideas with stories or representations.

Math Note

❸ **Subtraction on the Number Line** There are two ways to show subtraction on a number line. One model starts with the initial amount and then removes the amount to be subtracted, as in the number line shown for this discussion. In this representation, students start at $\$5.00$ and then jump back $\$2.00$, landing on $\$3.00$, which is the difference. In the other model, students would think of finding the distance on the number line *between* $\$5$ and $\$1.97$. In this case, the difference may be found by adding up or subtracting back. (For another example, see the number lines on page 135 in Session 3.6.) Keep in mind that students who are thinking in terms of just one of these models may have difficulty visualizing what is happening in the other model.

Let's see how we can use a story to show whether $5.00 − $1.97 leaves you with less money or more money than $5.00 − $2.00. Could someone tell a story about $5.00 − $2.00?

Students might say:

 "I had 5 dollar bills and I owed my friend 2 dollars, so I gave her 2 dollar bills, and I had 3 dollars left."

Now could someone tell the same story with $5.00 − $1.97? How would it be different?

Students might say:

 "I had 5 dollar bills and I owed my cousin $1.97. I didn't have any change so I gave her 2 dollar bills. But that was too much, so she gave me 3 cents back. Now I had 3 dollars and another 3 cents. It's different from the first story because I ended up with more!"

Give students another problem to consider:

$$\$3.00 - \$1.92$$

How can you make a problem with whole dollars to help you solve this problem?

Let students discuss this problem and find a solution before sending them off to do Math Workshop activities.

MATH WORKSHOP

2 Subtraction Problems About Money

40 MIN

In this Math Workshop, students finish the work they began yesterday with money problems. Those who have finished all the problems may play *Collections Compare*. You should also finish assessing all students on the subtraction facts.

2A How Much Change?

INDIVIDUALS PAIRS

For complete details about this activity, see Session 3.4, page 125.

2B Earning and Spending

INDIVIDUALS PAIRS

For complete details about this activity, see Session 3.4, page 126.

2C Assessment: Subtraction Facts

INDIVIDUALS

Continue to use either Subtraction Cards or Assessment: Subtraction Facts (M53) during this Math Workshop. If you cannot get to everyone during this time, plan to meet with the remaining students outside math class.

For complete details about this activity, see Session 3.4, page 127.

A student should be able to quickly answer each problem on the Subtraction Cards.

2D Collections Compare

PAIRS

For complete details about this activity, see Session 3.1, page 104.

SESSION FOLLOW-UP
3 Daily Practice

 Daily Practice: For ongoing review, have students complete *Student Activity Book* page 55.

 Student Math Handbook: Students and families may use *Student Math Handbook* pages 32–35 for reference and review. See pages 179–189 in the back of this unit.

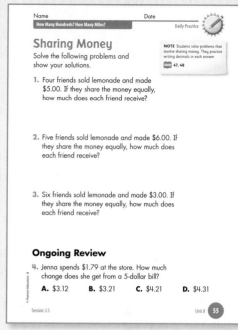

Name _____ Date _____

How Many Hundreds? How Many Miles?   Daily Practice

Sharing Money

Solve the following problems and show your solutions.

NOTE Students solve problems that involve sharing money. They practice writing decimals in each answer.

47, 48

1. Four friends sold lemonade and made $5.00. If they share the money equally, how much does each friend receive?

2. Five friends sold lemonade and made $6.00. If they share the money equally, how much does each friend receive?

3. Six friends sold lemonade and made $3.00. If they share the money equally, how much does each friend receive?

Ongoing Review

4. Jenna spends $1.79 at the store. How much change does she get from a 5-dollar bill?

   A. $3.12   **B.** $3.21   **C.** $4.21   **D.** $4.31

Session 3.5   Unit 8   55

▲ **Student Activity Book, p. 55**

Strategies for Subtraction

Math Focus Points

◆ Solving subtraction problems that involve comparison, removal, or finding a missing part

◆ Subtracting 3-digit numbers by using strategies that involve either subtracting one number in parts, adding up, or subtracting back

◆ Representing solutions to subtraction problems with number lines, 1,000 charts, and/or story contexts

Today's Plan		Materials
① ACTIVITY **Solving Subtraction Problems**	40 MIN INDIVIDUALS	• *Student Activity Book*, pp. 56–57
② DISCUSSION **Strategies for Subtraction**	20 MIN PAIRS CLASS	• Chart paper (as needed)
③ SESSION FOLLOW-UP **Daily Practice and Homework**		• *Student Activity Book*, pp. 58–59 • *Student Math Handbook*, pp. 32–35

Ten-Minute Math

Guess My Rule Choose a rule that describes kinds of places such as "places where you buy things". Inside a large circle, write the names of several places that fit the rule. As students suggest places that may or may not fit this rule, place them inside or outside the circle. Students deduce what the rule is from the evidence. After the rule has been established, ask students:

• Is the number of places that fit the rule more or less than two thirds of the total? How do you know?

Students discuss what is about two thirds of the total.

ACTIVITY

Solving Subtraction Problems

40 MIN INDIVIDUALS

Students solve subtraction problems on *Student Activity Book* pages 56–57. Included are story problems in each of the problem types that students have worked with in this investigation (removal, comparison, and finding a missing part), as well as subtraction equations.

ONGOING ASSESSMENT: Observing Students at Work

Students solve subtraction problems with 3-digit numbers.

- **Can students interpret each story problem situation and set up a correct solution strategy?**

- **If students are subtracting by breaking the numbers apart, are they making use of efficient "chunks" of numbers?**

- **If students are either adding up or subtracting back, what landmark numbers are they using as stopping-off places?** Are they using 100 and multiples of 100?

- **Do students compute accurately?**

- **Can students clearly show their thinking with mathematical notation?**

Continue to notice the strategies that students are using. Identify a few students who add up or subtract back from one number, as well as some who subtract in parts. Ask these students to be ready to share their solutions in the following discussion.

DIFFERENTIATION: Supporting the Range of Learners

Extension Some students may be ready to solve subtraction problems with larger numbers. Offer them problems with larger 3-digit numbers and numbers above 1,000. Ask these students to consider how their strategies are the same or different when they are working with larger numbers.

- **Do these students sometimes combine strategies, solving part of the problem in one way and another part in a different way?**

- **How do they keep track of their steps in problems with larger numbers?**

- **Are there ways that they could be more efficient?**

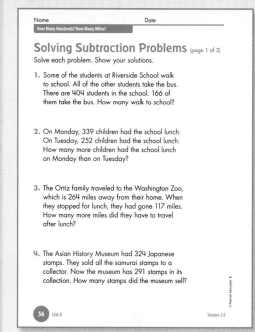

▲ Student Activity Book, p. 56

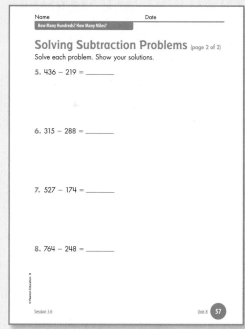

▲ Student Activity Book, p. 57

Teaching Note

❶ More- and Less-Efficient Strategies Some third graders need to carry out more in-between steps when they subtract a number in parts. For example, to solve 821 − 456, a student might carry out these steps:

$$821 - 400 = 421$$

$$421 - 20 = 401$$

$$401 - 1 = 400$$

$$400 - 30 = 370$$

$$370 - 5 = 365$$

This student breaks 50 into 20 + 30 and 6 into 1 + 5 in order to create easier subtraction problems. By the end of Grade 3, we encourage students to subtract larger "chunks" of numbers. However, for students who have had difficulty with subtraction, carefully using and keeping track of all the steps shown here may indicate excellent progress. For example, this student makes good decisions about which parts of 456 to subtract at each point in his procedure. You will have to judge which students are simply being "safe" and are actually ready to use larger chunks and which students still need to carry out more steps.

Students who are ready might test their subtraction strategies on problems with larger numbers.

DISCUSSION
2 Strategies for Subtraction

20 MIN   PAIRS   CLASS

Math Focus Points for Discussion

◆ Subtracting 3-digit numbers by using strategies that involve either subtracting one number in parts, adding up, or subtracting back

◆ Representing solutions to subtraction problems with number lines, 1,000 charts, and/or story contexts

Write 821 − 456 = _____ on the board and bring the class together for discussion. Give students a few minutes to solve the problem, talk with a partner about their solutions, and compare strategies.❶

As you talk with your partner, listen carefully to how each of you would solve this. Maybe you both would use the same or almost the same strategy, but maybe you would each solve it differently. When we come back together in a few minutes, be ready to explain not just your strategy, but your partner's as well.

Ask several students to share their strategies and talk about how their strategies compared with those of their partners. Record the reported strategies on chart paper.

Students might say:

"I did 821 minus 400 first—that's 421. Then minus 50 and that's 371. Minus 6 is 365. My partner got the same answer, but he added up: 456 plus 4 is 460, plus 40 to get to 500, and 321 to get to 821. 4 plus 40 plus 321 is 365—it works!"

(subtracting in parts)	(adding up in parts)
$821 - 400 = 421$	$456 + 4 = 460$
$421 - 50 = 371$	$460 + 40 = 500$
$371 - 6 = 365$	$500 + 321 = 821$
	$4 + 40 + 321 = 365$

"My partner and I both subtracted on a number line. We both started at 821, but she subtracted 456 in pieces, and I subtracted until I got to 456. She landed at 365, and I got 365 when I added up my jumps."

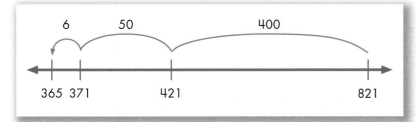

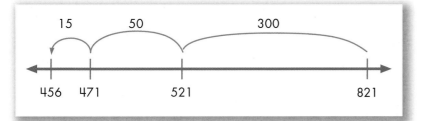

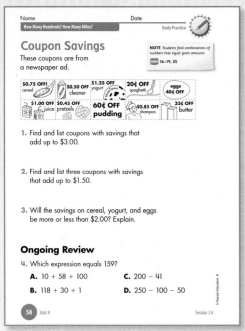

▲ Student Activity Book, p. 58

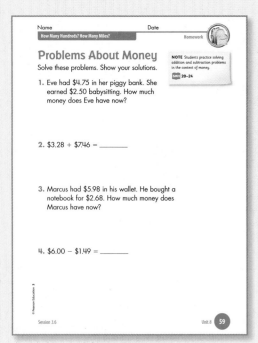

▲ Student Activity Book, p. 59

By the end of this discussion, you should have a representative set of students' subtraction strategies recorded on chart paper. Post these where students can refer to them as they continue to practice subtraction.

3 Daily Practice and Homework

 Daily Practice: For reinforcement of this unit's content, have students complete *Student Activity Book* page 58.

 Homework: On *Student Activity Book* page 59, students solve addition and subtraction problems that involve amounts of money.

 Student Math Handbook: Students and families may use *Student Math Handbook* pages 32–35 for reference and review. See pages 179–189 in the back of this unit.

What Combinations Can I Make?

Math Focus Points

◆ Solving addition problems with more than 2 addends

◆ Determining combinations of addends for a given sum

◆ Solving addition and subtraction problems with more than one step

Today's Plan		Materials
ACTIVITY ① **What Combinations Can I Make?** 15 MIN / CLASS		• Chart: "$100 for Supplies"*
MATH WORKSHOP ② **Addition and Subtraction with Money** ②A Book Orders ②B Two-Step Money Problems 45 MIN		②A • *Student Activity Book*, pp. 61–62 ②B • *Student Activity Book*, pp. 63–64 • Play money (as needed, optional)
SESSION FOLLOW-UP ③ **Daily Practice and Homework**		• *Student Activity Book*, pp. 65–66 • *Student Math Handbook*, pp. 20–24, 32–35

*See *Materials to Prepare,* p. 101.

Ten-Minute Math

Guess My Rule Choose a rule that describes a physical characteristic such as "curly hair". Select several students who fit the rule to stand in front of the class. Students guess who else fits the rule and who does not, and deduce what the rule is from the evidence. After the rule has been established, ask students:

• Is the number of students who fit the rule more or less than three fourths of the class? How do you know?

Students discuss what is about three fourths of the class.

Teaching Note

❶ Addition and Subtraction Together During this session, students solve two kinds of problems that involve using both addition and subtraction. In Book Orders, students are given a price list of books and find different combinations of titles they could buy with $10. They combine prices and then determine the difference between their total and $10. In Two-Step Money Problems, students solve problems that involve the exchange of money, usually by earning and spending different amounts. Both problem sets offer students the opportunity to apply the ideas they have been working on in this unit—addition and subtraction—and to consider how the operations are related to each other.

ACTIVITY

1 What Combinations Can 1 Make?

15 MIN   CLASS

To introduce the type of problems students will be solving in Book Orders, a Math Workshop activity, pose a similar type of problem to the class.❶

Suppose that our principal gave me $100 to buy supplies for our classroom, and you all can help me decide how to spend it. Here's a list of things we can buy and how much they cost.

Show the chart that you prepared.

$100 for Supplies	
Globe	$45
Crayons	$36
Scissors	$28
Fish tank	$72
Dictionary	$15
Soccer ball	$23
Microscope	$57

What combinations of two things can we buy? Without adding it up exactly, how do you know the sum doesn't go over $100?

Give students a few minutes to come up with a few combinations and share their thinking. Then pose this problem:

Are there combinations of more than two things here that we can buy for $100? How can you use some number relationships that you know to help you think about this?

As students offer suggestions, ask them to explain their thinking.

Students might say:

"If we buy the microscope, we've spent more than $50, so we have to find two other things that cost less than $50 together."

"If you look for small numbers in the 10s and add them up till you get to almost 100, you might go too high if you add all the 1s, so then you'd have to take something away."

Tell students that in today's Math Workshop, along with other money problems, they will be solving problems about making combinations that equal or come close to a certain amount of money.

 MATH WORKSHOP

Addition and Subtraction with Money

45 MIN

Students should spend time on both of these activities over the next two days of Math Workshop.

2A Book Orders

 INDIVIDUALS   PAIRS

Student may choose to work either with a partner or alone. Before work begins, briefly discuss *Student Activity Book* pages 61–62 with the class. If students are familiar with ordering books from book clubs in your classroom, you may want to make that connection. If not, explain that this list is like a catalog from which books can be ordered and received by mail.

ONGOING ASSESSMENT: Observing Students at Work

Students determine what possible combinations make up a given sum.

- **How do students approach these problems?** Do they begin with an estimate based on whole-dollar amounts that are close to the actual amounts? Do they use a combination of addition and subtraction to make adjustments to get as close to $10 as they can? Do some students use trial and error?

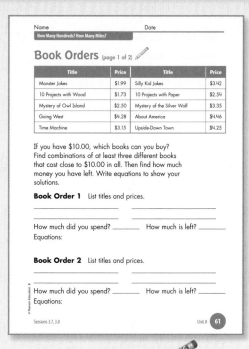

Name _____ Date _____
How Many Hundreds? How Many Miles?

Book Orders (page 1 of 2)

Title	Price	Title	Price
Monster Jokes	$1.99	Silly Kid Jokes	$3.42
10 Projects with Wood	$1.73	10 Projects with Paper	$2.54
Mystery of Owl Island	$2.50	Mystery of the Silver Wolf	$3.35
Going West	$4.28	About America	$4.46
Time Machine	$3.15	Upside-Down Town	$4.25

If you have $10.00, which books can you buy? Find combinations of at least three different books that cost close to $10.00 in all. Then find how much money you have left. Write equations to show your solutions.

Book Order 1 List titles and prices.

How much did you spend? _____ How much is left? _____
Equations:

Book Order 2 List titles and prices.

How much did you spend? _____ How much is left? _____
Equations:

Sessions 3.7, 3.8   Unit 8 **61**

▲ **Student Activity Book, p. 61**

Name _____ Date _____
How Many Hundreds? How Many Miles?

Book Orders (page 2 of 2)

Title	Price	Title	Price
Monster Jokes	$1.99	Silly Kid Jokes	$3.42
10 Projects with Wood	$1.73	10 Projects with Paper	$2.54
Mystery of Owl Island	$2.50	Mystery of the Silver Wolf	$3.35
Going West	$4.28	About America	$4.46
Time Machine	$3.15	Upside-Down Town	$4.25

Find other combinations of at least three different books that cost close to $10.00 in all. For one order, find a combination of at least four books.

Book Order 3 List titles and prices.

How much did you spend? _____ How much is left? _____
Equations:

Book Order 4 List titles and prices.

How much did you spend? _____ How much is left? _____
Equations:

62 Unit 8   Sessions 3.7, 3.8

▲ **Student Activity Book, p. 62**

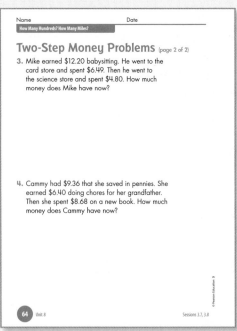

Two-Step Money Problems (page 1 of 2)

Solve these problems. Show your solutions.

1. Lakesha had $4.75 in her piggy bank. She spent $3.29 on a present for her sister. Then she earned $2.00 sweeping the front steps for a neighbor. How much money does Lakesha have now?

2. Greg had $8.15 in his wallet. He spent $5.87 on a sandwich. Then his friend paid him back $7.50 that he owed him. How much money does Greg have now?

▲ Student Activity Book, p. 63

Two-Step Money Problems (page 2 of 2)

3. Mike earned $12.20 babysitting. He went to the card store and spent $6.49. Then he went to the science store and spent $4.80. How much money does Mike have now?

4. Cammy had $9.36 that she saved in pennies. She earned $6.40 doing chores for her grandfather. Then she spent $8.68 on a new book. How much money does Cammy have now?

▲ Student Activity Book, p. 64

- **Can students add more than two amounts of money accurately?** Do they make good choices about what numbers or parts of numbers to add first?

- **Can students accurately find the difference between the sums they found and $10?**

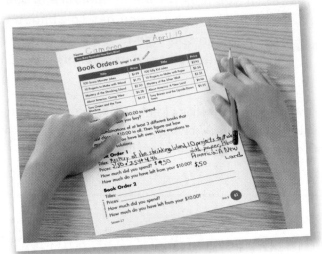

Rounding to whole-dollar amounts is a useful way to estimate money totals.

2B Two-Step Money Problems

INDIVIDUALS

All of the problems on *Student Activity Book* pages 63–64 involve more than one step. Students must solve the first part and then use that solution to solve the second part of the problem. Remind students that they will need to check their computation carefully and make sure that their answers for each part are reasonable.

ONGOING ASSESSMENT: Observing Students at Work

Students solve addition and subtraction problems with more than one step.

- **Do students recognize which parts of the problem involve addition and which parts involve subtraction?**

- **Do students make good choices about what part of the problem to do first?**

- **Do students use the strategies they choose for each part of the problem efficiently?** Do they notate their strategies clearly? Do they check their computation for accuracy and reasonableness?

DIFFERENTIATION: Supporting the Range of Learners

Intervention Some students may need help thinking through the actions of each problem and visualizing the amounts that are being added and subtracted. You could help these students by condensing the language of the problems and separating the two parts. You could rewrite Problem 1 this way:

> Lakesha had $4.75.
>
> She spent $3.29.
>
> She had _____ left over.
>
>
> So Lakesha had _____.
>
> She earned $2.00.
>
> Now she has _____.

You could also suggest that students act out what is happening with play money.

SESSION FOLLOW-UP
③ Daily Practice and Homework

 Daily Practice: For ongoing review, have students complete *Student Activity Book* page 65.

 Homework: On *Student Activity Book* page 66, students estimate and solve addition problems with more than two addends. They write an explanation of how they decided on their estimate.

 Student Math Handbook: Students and families may use *Student Math Handbook* pages 20–24, 32–35 for reference and review. See pages 179–189 in the back of this unit.

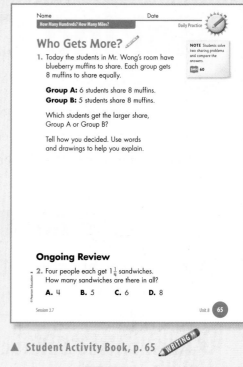

▲ Student Activity Book, p. 65

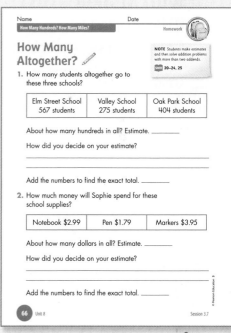

▲ Student Activity Book, p. 66

Making Combinations

Math Focus Points

◆ Solving addition problems with more than 2 addends

◆ Determining combinations of addends for a given sum

◆ Solving addition and subtraction problems with more than one step

Today's Plan		Materials
① DISCUSSION **What Combinations Did You Make?**	🕐 👥 20 MIN · CLASS	• *Student Activity Book*, p. 61 • Chart paper (optional)
② MATH WORKSHOP **Addition and Subtraction with Money** **②A** Book Orders **②B** Two-Step Money Problems	🕐 40 MIN	**②A** • *Student Activity Book*, pp. 61–62 **②B** • *Student Activity Book*, pp. 63–64 • Play money (as needed; optional)
③ SESSION FOLLOW-UP **Daily Practice**		• *Student Activity Book*, p. 67 • *Student Math Handbook*, pp. 20–24, 32–35

Ten-Minute Math

Guess My Rule Choose a rule that describes a type of living thing such as "birds". Inside a large circle, write the names of several things that fit the rule. As students suggest animals that may or may not fit this rule, place them inside or outside the circle. Students deduce what the rule is from the evidence. After the rule has been established, ask students:

• Is the number of animals that fit the rule more or less than one fourth of the total? How do you know?

Students discuss what is about one fourth of the total.

DISCUSSION

① What Combinations Did You Make?

20 MIN   CLASS

Math Focus Points for Discussion

◆ Determining combinations of addends for a given sum

Begin this session by asking students to share some of their solutions for making a book order with three titles from *Student Activity Book* page 61.

Who made a book order that added up to an amount that was very close to $10?

Collect one or two solutions, and record these on the board or chart paper.

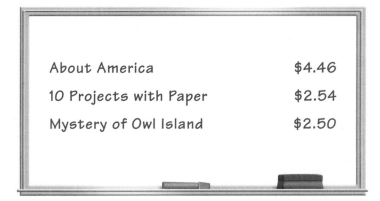

About America	$4.46
10 Projects with Paper	$2.54
Mystery of Owl Island	$2.50

Ask questions to help students explain their thinking about the process of choosing their books by price.

- How did you choose the numbers you added?

- What was the first book that you chose? After you chose that book, what size numbers were you looking for to choose your next books?

- How did you know that you weren't going to go over $10 with this order?

- Were there any numbers that you chose that didn't work? Why didn't they work?

In this discussion, listen for ways that students used estimation as they decided which numbers to add, which might include changing some prices to whole dollars (such as thinking of $1.99 as $2.00) and finding pairs of numbers that add up to a value close to a landmark (e.g., combinations that make a sum close to a dollar).

It seems that many of you were estimating as you chose your numbers. How did you keep track of how much your estimated numbers were over or under the actual prices?

Students might say:

"When I added $2.54 and $2.50, I knew that I had a little more than $5, so I had to find a book that was close to $5 but not more. That was okay, though, because there weren't any books that were more than $5!"

"I tried to pick one book for $4.46 and one book for $4.25—at first I thought that would be about $8, and then I could find a book for about $2. But the 46 cents and the 25 cents was a lot—almost 75 cents—and I couldn't find a book as cheap as $1.25."

Now write the following order on the board:

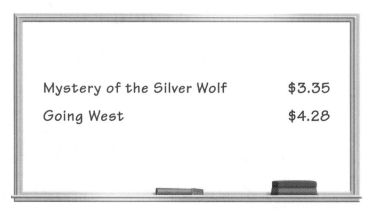

Mystery of the Silver Wolf $3.35

Going West $4.28

If these were the first two books I chose, could I also buy 10 Projects with Paper *for $2.54? Talk about this with your partner for a minute.*

Give students a minute or so to discuss this and then collect responses. Students should notice that the whole dollars add up to $9, but the cents add up to more than another dollar, putting the book order over $10.00.

What if I decided to buy Time Machine, *which costs $3.15, instead of* Mystery of the Silver Wolf, *which costs $3.35? Then could I buy* 10 Projects with Paper *for $2.54?*

Some students may be able to estimate that $3.15 is just enough less than $3.35 to keep the total of the cents within one dollar. Other students may need to carry out the actual computation. Collect both kinds of responses.

Point out to students that the strategies they have been discussing for this book order problem are just the kinds of strategies they could use while shopping in the supermarket or drugstore to make sure that they did not spend more money than they brought with them.

MATH WORKSHOP
Addition and Subtraction with Money

40 MIN

Students continue the two activities introduced in the last session and any unfinished *Student Activity Book* pages from earlier sessions.

2A Book Orders

INDIVIDUALS PAIRS

For complete details about this activity, see Session 3.7, page 139.

2B Two-Step Money Problems

INDIVIDUALS

For complete details about this activity, see Session 3.7, page 140.

Some students find it helpful to act out the problems with play money.

SESSION FOLLOW-UP
Daily Practice

Daily Practice: For reinforcement of this unit's content, have students complete *Student Activity Book* page 67.

Student Math Handbook: Students and families may use *Student Math Handbook* pages 20–24, 32–35 for reference and review. See pages 179–189 in the back of this unit.

Name _____ Date _____

How Many Hundreds? How Many Miles?   *Daily Practice*

Count Your Change
Complete this chart.

NOTE Students solve subtraction problems in the context of money.
SMH 32–35

Item Bought	Cost of Item	Amount Given to Clerk	Amount of Change
1. Ruler	$0.47	$1.00	
2. Sandwich	$3.18	$5.00	
3. Seeds	$1.55		$0.45
4. Socks	$2.74		$2.26
5. Shampoo		$1.00	$0.11
6. Taffy apple		$5.00	$4.10
7. Stickers	$1.16	$10.00	
8. Magazine		$10.00	$6.35

Ongoing Review

9. How much greater is 147 than 85?

  A. 43   **B.** 51   **C.** 53   **D.** 62

Session 3.8   Unit 8   **67**

▲ **Student Activity Book, p. 67**

End-of-Unit Assessment

Math Focus Points

◆ Solving addition problems with 3-digit numbers

◆ Solving addition problems with more than 2 addends

◆ Solving addition and subtraction problems with more than one step

◆ Subtracting 3-digit numbers by using strategies that involve either subtracting one number in parts, adding up, or subtracting back

Today's Plan		Materials
① ASSESSMENT ACTIVITY **End-of-Unit Assessment**	✔ 🕐 👤 **60 MIN INDIVIDUALS**	• M54–M55*
② SESSION FOLLOW-UP **Daily Practice**		• *Student Activity Book,* pp. 68–69 • *Student Math Handbook,* pp. 20–24, 32–35

*See *Materials to Prepare,* p. 101.

Ten-Minute Math

Guess My Rule Choose a rule that describes the clothing of some students, such as "wearing stripes" or "wearing pink". Select several students who fit the rule to stand in front of the class. Students guess who else fits the rule and who does not, and deduce what the rule is from the evidence. After the rule has been established, ask students:

• Is the number of students who fit the rule more or less than one third of the class? How do you know?

Students discuss what is about one third of the class. You might change the fraction to challenge your students.

ASSESSMENT ACTIVITY

1 End-of-Unit Assessment

60 MIN INDIVIDUALS

This End-of-Unit Assessment (M54–M55) assesses students on two of the unit's benchmarks.

Problem 1 asks students to solve a problem with three 3-digit addends. This problem addresses Benchmark 2: Solve 3-digit addition problems using at least one strategy efficiently.

Problems 2 and 3 ask students to find the difference between two money amounts. These problems address Benchmark 4: Solve subtraction problems with 3-digit numbers using strategies that involve either subtracting a number in parts, adding up, or subtracting back. ❶

ONGOING ASSESSMENT: Observing Students at Work

Students use their knowledge of addition and subtraction to solve the problems on the assessment.

- **Do students have an addition strategy that they can use efficiently?** Are their solutions accurate?

- **Do students have a subtraction strategy that they can use efficiently?** Are their solutions accurate?

- **Can students keep track of their solutions and record their thinking clearly with addition and subtraction notation?**

Although the assessment problems involve money amounts, students need not use money notation consistently in their solutions.

Professional Development

❶ **Teacher Note:** End-of-Unit Assessment, p. 171

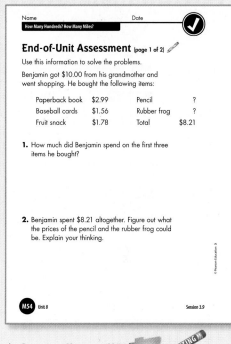

Name _____ Date _____

How Many Hundreds? How Many Miles?

End-of-Unit Assessment (page 1 of 2) ✏️

Use this information to solve the problems.

Benjamin got $10.00 from his grandmother and went shopping. He bought the following items:

Paperback book	$2.99	Pencil	?
Baseball cards	$1.56	Rubber frog	?
Fruit snack	$1.78	Total	$8.21

1. How much did Benjamin spend on the first three items he bought?

2. Benjamin spent $8.21 altogether. Figure out what the prices of the pencil and the rubber frog could be. Explain your thinking.

M54 Unit 8   Session 3.9

▲ **Resource Masters, M54** PORTFOLIO WRITING

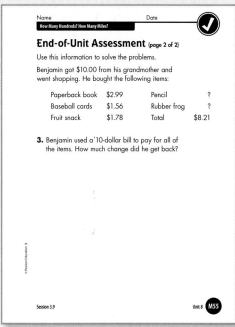

Name _____ Date _____

How Many Hundreds? How Many Miles?

End-of-Unit Assessment (page 2 of 2)

Use this information to solve the problems.

Benjamin got $10.00 from his grandmother and went shopping. He bought the following items:

Paperback book	$2.99	Pencil	?
Baseball cards	$1.56	Rubber frog	?
Fruit snack	$1.78	Total	$8.21

3. Benjamin used a 10-dollar bill to pay for all of the items. How much change did he get back?

Session 3.9   Unit 8 M55

▲ **Resource Masters, M55** PORTFOLIO

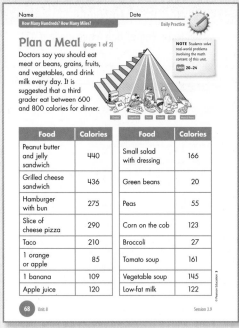

▲ Student Activity Book, p. 68

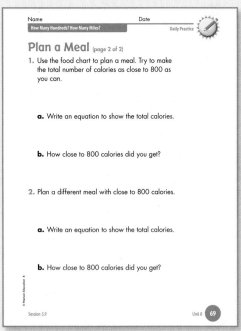

▲ Student Activity Book, p. 69

DIFFERENTIATION: Supporting the Range of Learners

Intervention If some students have trouble reading and understanding a problem, help them by restating it. For Problem 3, you could say:

If Benjamin started with $10 and spent $8.21, how much would he have left when he got back his change?

Note that such students need to continue working on interpreting addition and subtraction problems in context.

If some students can figure out the answer but are having trouble writing their strategy, encourage them to explain their thinking aloud. Help them choose words, mathematical expressions, and images to put their thoughts in writing. Note that these students may need ongoing support in recording their strategies for themselves.

SESSION FOLLOW-UP

2 Daily Practice

 Daily Practice: For enrichment, have students complete *Student Activity Book* pages 68–69. This practice provides real-world problems involving the math content of this unit.

 Student Math Handbook: Students and families may use *Student Math Handbook* pages 20–24, 32–35 for reference and review. See pages 181–189 in the back of this unit.

How Many Hundreds? How Many Miles?

In Part 6 of *Implementing Investigations in Grade 3* , you will find a set of Teacher Notes that addresses topics and issues applicable to the curriculum as a whole rather than to specific curriculum units. They include the following:

Computational Fluency and Place Value

Computational Algorithms and Methods

Representations and Contexts for Mathematical Work

Foundations of Algebra in the Elementary Grades

Discussing Mathematical Ideas

Racial and Linguistic Diversity in the Classroom: What Does Equity Mean in Today's Math Classroom?

Learning and Assessing Multiplication Combinations

Students are expected to learn the multiplication combinations with products to 50 by the end of Grade 3 and will be assessed on these combinations during this unit. They are expected to know the combinations through 12×12 by the end of Grade 4.

Although students work on the multiplication combinations throughout this unit, many students will need additional practice after this unit is completed. You can use the Multiplication Cards to do this. With your guidance about which multiplication combinations to work on, students should continue learning these combinations at home or outside math time. You may have other favorite practice methods or activities that you want to suggest for particular students. Also, enlist parents or other family members in helping with practice. This **Teacher Note** provides recommendations for supporting students in this ongoing practice.

Why Do We Call Them *Combinations*?

The pairs of factors from 1×1 through 12×12 are traditionally referred to as "multiplication facts"—the multiplication combinations with which students are expected to be fluent. The *Investigations* curriculum follows the National Council of Teachers of Mathematics (NCTM) convention of calling these expressions *combinations* rather than *facts*. *Investigations* does this for two reasons. First, naming *only* particular addition and multiplication combinations as *facts* seems to give them elevated status, more important than other critical parts of mathematics. In addition, the word *fact* implies that something cannot be learned through reasoning. For example, it is a fact that the first president of the United States was George Washington, and it is a fact that Rosa Parks was born in Alabama in 1913. If these facts are important for us to know, we can remember them or use reference materials to look them up. However, the product for the multiplication combination

6×7 can be determined in many ways; it is logically connected to our system of numbers and operations. If we forget the product, but understand what multiplication is and know some related multiplication combinations, we can find the product through reasoning. For example, if we know that $5 \times 7 = 35$, we can add one more 7 to determine that the product of 6×7 is 42. If we know that $3 \times 7 = 21$, we can reason that the product of 6×7 would be twice that, $2 \times (3 \times 7) = 42$.

The term *facts* does convey a meaning that is generally understood by some students and family members. Thus, you will need to decide whether to use the term *facts* along with *combinations* in certain settings in order to make your meaning clear.

Fluency with Multiplication Combinations

Like NCTM, this curriculum supports the importance of students learning the basic combinations fluently through a focus on reasoning about number relationships: "Fluency with whole-number computation depends, in large part, on fluency with basic number combinations—the single digit addition and multiplication pairs and their counterparts for subtraction and division. Fluency with basic number combinations develops from well-understood meanings for the four operations and from a focus on thinking strategies. . . ." [*Principles and Standards for School Mathematics*, pp. 152–153]

Fluency means that combinations are quickly accessible mentally, either because they are immediately known or because the calculation that is used is so effortless as to be essentially automatic (in the way that some adults quickly derive one combination from another).

Helping Students Learn the Multiplication Combinations

Combinations with Products to 50

For many students starting out in Grade 3, learning multiplication combinations may seem overwhelming—an endless mass of combinations with no order and reason. It is essential to bring order and reason to students' learning of multiplication combinations in a way that lets them have control over their progress. Traditionally, students learned one "table" at a time—first the $\times 2$ combinations, then the $\times 3$ combinations, the $\times 4$ combinations, and so on. However, the multiplication combinations can be grouped in other ways to support learning related combinations.

First make sure that students know all multiplication combinations that involve $\times 0$, $\times 1$, $\times 2$, $\times 5$, and $\times 10$ (up to 10×10) fluently. *Note that although most third graders can easily count by 2, 5, and 10, the student who is fluent does not need to skip count to determine the product of multiplication combinations involving these numbers.* Knowing that multiplication is commutative is crucial for learning all the multiplication combinations. The work with Array Cards supports this understanding (see the **Teacher Note:** Representing Multiplication with Arrays in Unit 5, *Equal Groups*). When these combinations are known, provide students with a sequence of small groups of the multiplication combinations they still need to review so that they can relate to what they already know. There are a number of ways to do this. Here is one we recommend:

1. Learning the $\times 4$ combinations. Work on the $\times 4$ combinations that students do not yet know: 3×4, 4×4, 6×4, 7×4, 8×4, and 9×4 (and 4×3, 4×6, and so on). Help students think of these as doubling the $\times 2$ combinations: $4 \times 6 = (2 \times 6) + (2 \times 6)$ or $4 \times 6 = 2 \times (2 \times 6)$. Students may verbalize this idea as "4 times 6 is 2 times 6 and another 2 times 6" or "to get 4 times 6, I double 2×6." Doubling is also useful within the $\times 4$ combinations (for example, when students know that $3 \times 4 = 12$, then that fact can be used to solve 6×4: $6 \times 4 = (3 \times 4) + (3 \times 4)$). Getting used to thinking

about doubling with smaller numbers will also prepare students for using this approach with some of the harder combinations.

2. Learning the square numbers. Next, students learn or review the three remaining combinations that produce square numbers less than 50: 3×3, 6×6, and 7×7. These are often easy for students to remember. If needed, use doubling or a known fact for "start with" clues during practice. For example, 6×6 is double 3×6; $7 \times 7 = (4 \times 7) + (3 \times 7)$. Students can also build these with tiles or draw them on grid paper to see how they can be represented by squares.

3. Learning the remaining facts with products to 50. Finally, learn or review the six remaining facts with products to 50: 3×6 through 3×9, 7×6, and 8×6. First relate them to known facts (e.g., double 3×3 or halve 6×6 to get 3×6) and then practice them.

Although our benchmark is for third-graders to learn the combinations to 50, some third-graders will go beyond that benchmark. For example, most will learn the $\times 10$ combinations through 100, and many will use the patterns of the $\times 11$ and $\times 12$ combinations to learn these through 100 as well. Some students may be ready and eager to learn more.

Students Who Know Their Combinations to 50

This is not the focus in Grade 3, but students who know their combinations to 50 and the combinations that involve multiplying by 10 up to 100 (6×10, 7×10, 8×10, 9×10, 10×10), can work on learning the more difficult combinations. Here is one way of sequencing this work:

1. Learning the remaining combinations with products to 100. There are six difficult combinations to learn (other than the $\times 11$ and $\times 12$ combinations, which are, in fact, not as difficult as these, and are discussed below). These six difficult combinations are: 6×9 (and 9×6), 7×8 (and 8×7), 7×9 (and 9×7), 8×8, 8×9 (and 9×8), and 9×9.

Students can work on one or two of these most difficult multiplication combinations each week. Make sure that they use combinations they do know to help them learn ones they do not know—for example, $8 \times 7 = 2 \times (4 \times 7)$ or $9 \times 7 = (10 \times 7) - 7$. They can write these related multiplication combinations as "start with" hints on the Multiplication Cards. If most of your class needs to work on the same few hard combinations, you may want to assign the whole class to focus on two of these each week.

2. Learning the $\times$ 11 and $\times$ 12 combinations. We consider these combinations to be in a different category. Historically, these combinations were included in the list of multiplication facts. However, when we are dealing with 2-digit numbers in multiplication, an efficient way to solve them is through applying the distributive property, breaking the numbers apart by place as you would with any other 2-digit numbers. We include them here because some local or state frameworks still require knowing multiplication combinations through 12×12. In addition, 12 is a number that occurs often in our culture, and it is useful to know the $\times$ 12 combinations fluently. Most students learn the $\times$ 11 combinations easily because of the pattern, 11, 22, 33, 44, 55, . . . created by multiplying successive whole numbers by 11. They should also think through why this pattern occurs: $3 \times 11 = (3 \times 10) + (3 \times 1) = 30 + 3 = 33$. They should think through why $11 \times 10 = 110$ and $11 \times 11 = 121$ by breaking up the numbers. Students can learn the $\times$ 12 combinations by breaking the 12 into a 10 and 2; for example, $12 \times 6 = (10 \times 6) + (2 \times 6)$. Some students may also want to use doubling or adding on to known combinations: $12 \times 6 = 2 \times (6 \times 6)$ or $12 \times 6 = (11 \times 6) + 6$.

Fluency Benchmarks for Learning Facts Through the Grades

Addition: fluency by the end of Grade 2 with review and practice in Grade 3

Subtraction: fluency by the end of Grade 3 with review and practice in Grade 4

Multiplication: fluency with multiplication combinations with products to 50 by the end of Grade 3; up to 12×12 by the middle of Grade 4, with continued review and practice

Division: fluency by the end of Grade 5

Addition Strategies

Students' strategies for addition fall into two basic categories: (1) breaking the numbers apart and then adding these parts, and (2) changing the numbers to numbers that are easier to add. In order to use these strategies, students must understand the meaning of addition and have a good mental model of what is happening in the problem. They must be able to look at the problem as a whole, think about the relationships of the numbers in the problem, and choose an approach that they can carry out easily and accurately.

By the end of this unit, third-graders should be able to break apart 3-digit numbers in a variety of ways, add the parts accurately, keep track of all the parts of a problem, and combine the parts to find the sum of the original problem. They should feel comfortable and confident with at least one strategy and should be using it efficiently—adding the largest or most reasonable parts of the number and using a minimum number of steps. They should also be familiar with strategies that involve changing the numbers to create an easier problem to solve and should be able to adjust accurately for the change.

Below are examples of students' strategies for solving the following problem:

$$349 + 175 =$$

Although the steps for each strategy are all written out in this **Teacher Note,** in practice students gradually learn to carry out many of these steps mentally, jotting down just what they need to keep track of partial sums.

Breaking the Numbers Apart

In strategies that involve breaking numbers apart and then adding the parts, students use their understanding of the ways in which numbers can be decomposed to solve the problem.

Set A, Adding by place In the solutions in Set A, students break the numbers apart by place value, add each place, and then find a final total. Students often call these approaches "adding by place" or "adding 100s, 10s, and 1s."

$$349 + 175 =$$

Philip's strategy
$300 + 100 = 400$
$40 + 70 = 110$
$9 + 5 = 14$
$400 + 110 + 14 = 524$

Chiang's strategy
$300 + 100 = 400$
$30 + 70 = 100$
$10 + 100 = 110$
$9 + 5 = 14$
$400 + 110 + 14 = 524$

Philip started with the largest place, adding 100s, then 10s, then 1s. Chiang did the same, but further broke 40 into 30 and 10 in order to use the known combination $70 + 30$. This is an example of a step that students can learn to carry out mentally.

Students should also become familiar with vertical notation for this method:

$$
\begin{array}{rl}
349 & \\
+\ 175 & \\
\hline
400 & (300 + 100) \\
110 & (40 + 70) \\
\underline{14} & (9 + 5) \\
524 &
\end{array}
\qquad
\begin{array}{rl}
349 & \\
+\ 175 & \\
\hline
14 & (9 + 5) \\
110 & (40 + 70) \\
\underline{400} & (300 + 100) \\
524 &
\end{array}
$$

The expressions next to each partial sum indicate which parts of the numbers are added. Recording these expressions helps students understand the vertical notation, but students are not expected to include these expressions in their own notation.

Place-value models, such as 100 grids or stickers that come in sheets of 100, strips of 10, and single stickers, help students visualize what is happening when the numbers are broken apart by place and then added. For example, a student might describe part of the problem 349 + 175 this way:

"When I had to add 40 plus 70, I thought of it as 4 strips of (10) stickers and 7 strips. Three strips and seven strips make 10 strips, and 10 strips is a whole sheet (of 100). Then there's one strip left over—it's a hundred and ten (110)."

The U.S. regrouping algorithm, which some third-grade students may know, is also an example of adding by place. Rather than beginning with the largest place, as students often do naturally, this algorithm begins with the smallest place. It also includes a shorthand way of notating the value of the numbers as the digits in each place are added. For many third-graders, the compressed notation of this algorithm can obscure both the place value of the numbers and the meaning of each step. This can lead to a more rote approach to solving addition problems when students are solidifying their understanding of the base-ten number system and the operation of addition in Grade 3—steps in students' development of computational fluency that take time and practice.

After students have developed good, efficient algorithms that they understand and can carry out easily, such as adding by place, some may also become fluent in this traditional algorithm. Others will continue to use adding by place or adding on in parts fluently, which will also serve them well for their computation needs now and as adults. The "carrying" algorithm is not addressed directly in Grade 3, although some students may be able to use it with understanding. Note that the vertical notation of adding by place shown on the whiteboard, where the ones are added first, is closely related to the steps in the standard algorithm but makes these steps more transparent. When

students use the standard algorithm, demonstrate this form of notation and help students compare the two. Students who use the standard algorithm should also learn other strategies that demonstrate their flexibility with and understanding of addition. The U.S. algorithm is included in a study of strategies for addition in Grade 4.

Set B, Adding one number in parts In Set B, students break up one of the addends into parts and then add these parts, one at a time, to the other number. Students may refer to this set of solutions as "adding one number in parts."

$$349 + 175 =$$

Jane's strategy	Adam's strategy	Gina's strategy
349 + 100 = 449	349 + 100 = 449	175 + 300 = 475
449 + 70 = 519	449 + 50 = 499	475 + 25 = 500
519 + 5 = 524	499 + 25 = 524	500 + 24 = 524

Jane and Adam started with 349 but broke 175 up in different ways (100 + 70 + 5 and 100 + 50 + 25). Gina started with 175 instead and broke up 349 (300 + 25 + 24). When students use this strategy, they should be encouraged to add the largest "chunks" of numbers possible while still making sense of the problem and the numbers. Students often use a number line to represent their thinking when using this strategy.

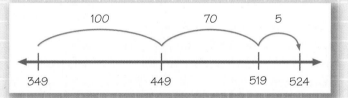

Changing the Numbers

In this category of addition strategies, students change one or both of the numbers to what they may call "landmark" or "friendly" numbers—generally multiples of 10 or 100. These strategies require that students understand how to compensate for any changes they make. Because many third-graders are still solidifying that understanding, you may find that these strategies are not yet accessible to all students. They should nonetheless be explored and discussed when the numbers in the problem lend themselves to this approach. Addition strategies that involve changing the numbers will be explored further in Grade 4.

Set A, Changing the numbers and adjusting the sum

In Set A, students change the numbers to multiples of 10 to create easier addition problems. Students often call this kind of solution "changing to a landmark."

$$349 + 175 =$$

Kelly's strategy
350 + 175 = 525
525 − 1 = 524

Elena's strategy
349 + 200 = 549
549 − 25 = 524

Denzel's strategy
350 + 200 = 550
550 − 25 − 1 = 524

After students have changed one or both numbers to a landmark and found the sum, they have to decide what to do to the sum to compensate for their initial changes. Kelly simply added 1 to 349, and then had to subtract 1 to get the final answer. Elena used a similar strategy, adding 25 to 175, then subtracting 25 at the end. Denzel changed both numbers to landmarks by adding 1 and 25, added them, then subtracted the 25 and the 1 that had been added.

Note that, as in other examples in this **Teacher Note,** students may carry out other in-between steps either mentally or in written form. For example, the first student might add 350 and 175 by adding on parts of 175 to 350: 350 + 50 + 100 + 25.

Set B, Creating an equivalent problem

Sometimes students change the numbers in an addition problem to create an equivalent problem that is easier to solve.

$$349 + 175 =$$

Benjamin's strategy
324 + 200 = 524

Keisha's strategy
400 + 124 = 524

In these examples, an increase in one addend is matched by an equal decrease in the other addend so that no additional adjustment is needed after the total has been found. Benjamin subtracted 25 from 349 and added 25 to 175; Keisha added and subtracted 51.

In these solutions for this particular problem, creating an equivalent problem that is easier to solve requires adding and subtracting either 25 or 51. It is more likely that third-graders would save this method for a problem in which a very small number, typically 1 or 2, must be added and subtracted. For example, students might change 398 + 175 to the equivalent expression 400 + 173.

Creating equivalent problems that are easier to solve is addressed in this unit for the first time and will be revisited in Grade 4.

Does Order Matter in Addition?

In third grade, the question of order in addition can come up for students in a variety of situations.

- When representing addition problems with stickers and strips: "26 + 52 and 52 + 26 are both 7 strips and 8 singles."

- When working on the activity *How Many More Stickers to Get 100?* "If I start with 48, I need 52. If I start with 52, I need 48."

- When adding more than two numbers, for example, 34 + 23 + 16: "I did it this way: 34 + 16 is 50, and 50 + 23 = 73."

Many students already realize that when the order of the addends in an addition problem changes, the sum does not. They may explain that this happens because you are just changing the placement of the numbers, but "you are not adding any more or taking anything away."

From a formal mathematical perspective, the ideas these students are working on involve two basic properties of arithmetic. The first is the *commutative property of addition,* which states that two numbers added in either order yield the same sum. Some students call these "opposites," or "switch-arounds," or "reversibles." The very fact that students have given names to this phenomenon indicates that they have formulated a generalization: If you take two numbers and switch them around, you still get the same sum when you add them. Written algebraically, this property can be expressed as $a + b = b + a$.

The second basic property, the *associative property of addition,* states that when three numbers are added together, they can be regrouped without changing the order and will yield the same sum. For example, $(35 + 14) + 6 = 35 + (14 + 6)$. In the expression to the left, first add 35 + 14 to get 49, and then add 49 + 6. In the expression to the right, first add 14 + 6 to get 20, and then add 35 + 20. (Using parentheses indicates that the operation within the parentheses is to be carried out first.) The sum for both is 55. Written algebraically, this property can be expressed as $(a + b) + c = a + (b + c)$. One calculation is easier than the other; the associative property guarantees that the sum is constant.

When performing addition with two numbers, the commutative property applies. When adding three or more numbers, the reordering might involve the commutative property, the associative property, or both in combination. It is not important for students to learn the formal names of these properties. Rather, they should be encouraged to examine questions about order, and to support their reasoning with various ways to represent addition—such as combining stickers and strips, story contexts, drawings of the situations, number lines, or 100 charts.

As students continue to learn about operations and calculations, questions about order will repeatedly arise: Does order matter when you subtract? What about when you multiply? What about when you divide? (They will find that it does matter when subtracting or dividing but not when adding or multiplying.) Does it matter when you add fractions or integers (which include numbers below zero)? Answering these questions is work ahead of your students in the months and years to come.

Assessment: Addition Strategies

Problems 1 and 2

Benchmark addressed:

Benchmark 2: Solve 3-digit addition problems using at least one strategy efficiently.

In order to meet the benchmark, student's work should show that they can:

• Use at least one of the following addition strategies accurately and efficiently:

—Break the numbers apart by place value and recombine them

—Add one number in parts that include multiples of 10 rather than a series of 10s (e.g., 172 + 30 rather than 172 + 10 + 10 + 10)

—Change the numbers to make an expression that is easier to solve and adjust for the change

• Record their strategies clearly, using addition notation and/or a number line representation.

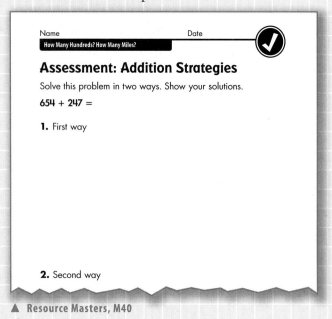

▲ Resource Masters, M40

Meeting the Benchmark

Students who meet the benchmark demonstrate that they can choose one of the strategies they have been working with, use that strategy accurately and efficiently, and record their thinking clearly. Although students are asked to solve the problem in more than one way, only one of their solutions must be accurate and efficient in order for them to meet the benchmark.

However, you can learn a great deal about how students are developing flexibility in their computation and understanding of the operation of addition from how they approach the problem the second time. Do they choose two different strategies (such as breaking the numbers apart by place value for their first way and adding one number in parts for their second way)? Do they use variations of the same strategy, such as breaking the numbers apart in different ways or making two different equivalent expressions? Students will be assessed on their flexibility with more than one addition strategy in Grade 4.

Becky first solved the problem with a place-value strategy. For her second solution, she added 654 on in two parts: first 650 and then 4. Both of Becky's strategies are efficient and clear.

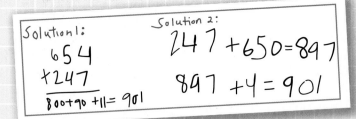

Becky's Work

The teacher knows from Becky's class work that she does many of the steps in a problem mentally. However, if you are unsure of how a student is carrying out intermediate steps—for example, how she is adding 247 and 650 mentally—ask the student to describe what she does in her head.

Dwayne also used place value for his first strategy. For his second strategy he wrote the equivalent expression 651 + 250. When asked by his teacher where he got those two numbers, he explained that he took 3 from 654 and "gave it" to 247 to make 250.

Solution 1:
$$600 + 200 = 800$$
$$50 + 40 = 90$$
$$7 + 4 = 11$$
$$800 + 90 + 11 = 901$$

Solution 2:
$$651 + 250 = 901$$

Dwayne's Work

Keisha broke the numbers apart in different ways in her two strategies. First she used a combination that results in a multiple of 100, 654 + 246, and then had to add 1 more from 247. For her second solution, she added the multiples of 10 in the problem, 650 + 240, and then added each ones digit separately. Keisha demonstrates that she can think quite flexibly about ways to break numbers apart and that she has a good grasp of combinations of 2-digit numbers that equal 100.

Solution 1:
$$654 + 246 = 900$$
$$900 + 1 = 901$$

Solution 2:
$$650 + 240 = 890$$
$$890 + 7 = 897$$
$$897 + 4 = 901$$

Keisha's Work

Partially Meeting the Benchmark

Some students may have a solid understanding of addition with 3-digit numbers but may have either made a computation error or used an accurate but inefficient solution, such as adding individual 10s rather than adding multiples of 10. These students partially meet the benchmark. When students' work shows incorrect computation, ask whether they have double-checked their work. Determine whether the student needs to review a few addition combinations, lost track of a step in the procedure, misread a number, or simply made a mistake through inattention. If students are using good strategies but using them less efficiently than you would like, ask whether they can combine steps.

In both of Edwin's strategies, he loses track of the 7 in 247. In his first attempt, Edwin adds the 100s and then adds on the 2-digit parts of the numbers. He adds 54 (from 654) and then two chunks of 20, presumably from the 47 in 247. He leaves out the 7 and comes up with an incorrect answer, 894. Note that Edwin's notation of adding on after the equal sign is not mathematically accurate because it does not indicate equivalent expressions.

Solution 1:
$600 + 200 = 800 + 54 = 854 + 20 = 874 + 20 = 894$

Solution 2:
$54 + 20 = 74 + 20 = 94$
$600 + 200 = 800 + 94 = 894$

Edwin's Work

Edwin also seems to lack confidence in adding on multiples of 10 because he breaks up 40 into $20 + 20$ rather than adding 40 on directly.

If students are losing track of parts of their strategies, as Edwin does, ask them to go back and check to make sure that they have accounted for all parts of the numbers that resulted from breaking the numbers apart.

Gina changed the numbers in the problem by making the expression $654 + 250$. She seems to know that she has to make an adjustment for the 3 that was added to 247 to get 250, but she incorrectly adds it instead of subtracting it.

Solution 1:
$654 + 250 = 904$
$904 + 3 = 907$

Solution 2:
$657 + 250 = 907$

Gina's Work

It is likely that Gina should be working on a strategy that involves breaking the numbers apart, rather than this one, as her primary strategy. Until she can accurately and efficiently solve a multidigit addition problem with the numbers as they are given, she should probably not be working with a strategy that involves changing the numbers. However, if Gina has another efficient and accurate strategy, she can use that strategy to double-check her answers as she is thinking through this new approach. Putting the problem in a context will also help her reason about how the sum must be adjusted when she changes one of the numbers in the problem.

Keep in mind that if students are making mistakes similar to Gina's and Edwin's on one strategy, they are likely to correct themselves when they solve the problem a second way and come up with a different answer. In that case, they do meet the benchmark, because they are required to demonstrate one accurate and efficient strategy for this assessment.

It is not unusual, however, for some third-graders to "believe" their first answer and to make their second solution somehow come out with the same incorrect answer. Both Gina and Edwin did this. Gina justified her answer by writing an equivalent expression for her second solution, $657 + 250$, rather than solving the problem with a different strategy. Edwin broke the numbers apart in the same way for his second solution but added them in a different order and with slightly different notation, again leaving out the 7. He may have decided to stop when he got the answer he expected, 894.

Continue to give these students addition problems to solve, encouraging them to pay careful attention to each step in their solutions. These students may also benefit from solving more Addition Starter Problems so that they have an opportunity to increase their flexibility with different strategies.

Not Meeting the Benchmark

Some students may not yet have one strategy that they can use accurately. Evidence of this could include adding by counting up in very small chunks (by 10s and/or 1s) and losing track; relying on using a representation such as a number line or 100 grids as the only strategy; or not being able to accurately break 3-digit numbers apart and keep track of the parts.

Adam attempted to use a number line and began by adding 3 to 247 to get to a multiple of 10. He then jumped by 10s (one of which he labeled as 20) until he reached 300, and then he made a jump of 300 and a jump of 54 to get to 654. Adam has confused the operations of addition and subtraction here by finding the difference between the two numbers rather than adding them. He did not add his jumps together to get a final solution and therefore could not check the reasonableness of his answer. Adam did not offer a second solution on his paper.

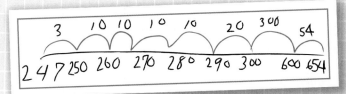

Adam's Work

These students will need to continue to practice whichever strategy is most accessible to them. In many cases, this is likely to be breaking the numbers apart by place and recombining them. Continue to model this strategy for these students, help them visualize what is happening as they add parts of numbers, and provide opportunities for practice so that they gain proficiency with one strategy. Talk through the problem using an addition context that is familiar to them: "200 of the 247 people in one line have gone into the movie theater, and 600 of the 654 people from the other line have gone into the theater. How many people are left in the first line? In the second line? Which group of people do you want to let in next?"

A few students may not yet have a solid understanding of place value, which makes it difficult to keep track of the value of each part of the numbers when solving an addition problem with multidigit numbers. These students may need to continue working with representing addition of 2- and 3-digit numbers with a visual model of place value, such as the sticker context. They can also benefit from continuing to play any of the *Capture* games, either from this or previous addition and subtraction units.

Teacher Note

Types of Subtraction Situations

In this unit, students encounter three categories of subtraction situations. All of these are situations that are commonly encountered in the world and that subtraction can be used to solve. Students should be able to visualize each type of problem situation and apply subtraction (or, in some cases, addition) to solve them.

The way students visualize each type of situation may lead to particular strategies for solving the problem that seem to the student to best match the action or characteristics of the situation. In Grades 3 and 4, students will also be developing recognition that they can apply any subtraction strategy to any of these situations.

Here are the three types of situations students encounter in the story problems in this unit:

1. Removal

This type of subtraction situation is the one students first become familiar with in the early grades. They often refer to this kind of situation as "take away" because some quantity is removed or "taken away" from a larger amount. For example, some of the sticker problems in the first Grade 3 addition and subtraction unit, *Trading Stickers, Combining Coins,* involve removal:

Gil had 85 stickers. He gave 47 stickers to his cousin. How many stickers does he have now?

This type of subtraction situation is characterized by an action in which part of a quantity is removed in any number of ways—spent, eaten, lost, given away, used up, and so forth. Matching this action, students often think about solving a removal problem by subtracting in parts:

$$85 - 40 = 45$$

$$45 - 5 = 40$$

$$40 - 2 = 38$$

Problems in this category differ in terms of which quantities are given and which quantity must be determined. For example, the problem above might be altered to solve for either the starting amount or the amount removed:

Gil had some stickers. He gave 47 stickers to his cousin. Then he had 38 stickers left. How many stickers did Gil have to start?

Gil had 85 stickers. He gave some to his cousin. Then he had 38 left. How many stickers did he give to his cousin?

Students typically find these problems more difficult to visualize and solve than the simple removal problem. In the first case, they have to work backwards from the amounts used and remaining to determine the initial quantity (this is actually solved by addition). In the second case, students have to figure out that they have to remove the remaining amount from the initial quantity in order to determine the amount used.

2. Comparison

Problems in this category involve questions such as "how much more?" and "how much less?" The Comparing Collections: How Many More? problems in Unit 3, Investigation 4 involve comparison. Here is an example (*Student Activity Book* page 67, Problem 3).

Ms. Santos' class collected 86 bottle caps in the first two days of their Class Collection. Mr. Singh's class collected 123 bottle caps. How many more bottle caps did Mr. Singh's class collect than Ms. Santos' class?

In this type of problem, two different quantities are compared, unlike the previous category in which one quantity is initially part of the other. Students often visualize comparison as one quantity lined up next to the other—as you might visualize comparing the heights of two people.

Matching the image of the problem, they may think about adding up to find out how much more one quantity is than the other, or subtracting back to find out how much less one quantity is than the other.

There are two types of problems in this category, problems like the one above in which two quantities are given, or problems in which one quantity and the difference from the other quantity are given, for example:

Mr. Singh's class collected 123 bottle caps in the first two days of their class collection. Ms. Santos' class collected 37 fewer bottle caps than Mr. Singh's class. How many bottle caps did Ms. Santos' class collect?

3. Missing part

In this situation, a quantity is divided into two parts. The Travel Story problems in Unit 3, Investigation 3 are missing part problems. Here is an example (*Student Activity Book* page 59, Problem 1).

Philip and Keith are on a 3-day biking trip. Their final destination is 138 miles away. On the first day, they rode 51 miles. How much farther do they have to bike?

In this case, the whole quantity is the number of miles from the start to the final destination. This situation is not one of removal: there is no *action* of giving away or using up. Rather, we are considering *two* parts of the total mileage, the part already traveled and the part remaining to be traveled.

As in comparison problems, students often think of starting with one of the parts and adding up to the whole quantity. They might notate such problems as missing addend problems and solve them by adding up:

$$51 + \underline{\hspace{1cm}} = 138$$

There is only one type of problem in this category: the whole and one part are given, and the other part must be determined. (If both parts are given, and the problem is to determine the whole, the problem is categorized as addition, not subtraction.)

Solving problems in any category

We have named these categories in order to be able to describe them, but it is not necessary for students to name these categories or say to which category a problem belongs. What is important is that they can visualize the relationship between the quantities in all three types of situation, regardless of which quantities are given and which must be determined, and can then apply the operation of subtraction (or addition) appropriately. Some of these problem types may be easier for students than others. They have been familiar with removal situations for many years; they may have a harder time visualizing comparison and missing part problems.

There are many similarities, as well as differences, between these three types of situation. While the actions in the situations differ, they all involve the difference between two quantities. When unfamiliar with a problem type, students are more likely to select a method that closely matches the action of the problem. As students become more familiar and flexible with all of these situations, they can apply any solution strategy to a problem of any type. For example, students might solve the removal problem above by adding up or the missing part problem by subtracting in parts. (See the **Teacher Note:** Subtraction Strategies, page 163.)

Learning and Assessing Subtraction Facts Related to Addition Combinations up to 10 + 10

To develop efficient computation strategies, students need to become fluent with the addition combinations from 1 + 1 to 10 + 10 and their related subtraction problems (i.e., 8 − 3, 10 − 6, 15 − 7, and so on.). Fluency with addition combinations and related subtraction facts means that these are quickly accessible mentally, either because they are immediately known or because the calculation that is used is so effortless as to be essentially automatic. In Investigations, all students should be fluent with all of the addition combinations up to 10 + 10 by the end of Grade 2. In Grade 3, students are expected to become fluent with the subtraction problems that are related to these addition combinations. In referring to these related subtraction problems, which cannot accurately be called combinations, it is often easier and more readily understandable to refer to them as facts.

Learning Subtraction Facts Fluently

The *Investigations* curriculum supports the importance of students' learning the basic facts fluently through a focus on reasoning about number relationships, not simply by rote memorization. Relying on memory alone is not sufficient. If your learning is based on understanding of numbers and their relationships, you have a way to rethink and restructure your knowledge when you do not remember something.

An important aspect to learning subtraction facts is to have an understanding of the inverse relationship between addition and subtraction. When students have fluency with the addition combinations, they can construct the related subtraction problems by thinking about how subtraction situations are related to adddition situations. Consider these examples:

Kim had 15 marbles and gave away 8. How many does she have left?

Elena is growing a bean plant. Last week, it was 8 inches tall. This week, it is 15 inches tall. How many inches did the plant grow since last week?

These situations can be represented with the equations 15 − 8 = _____ or 8 + _____ = 15. If students are fluent with addition combinations, they have a strategy for solving the subtraction problem based on a known number relationship, that is, the related addition combination. With practice, students can access this quickly and become equally fluent with these subtraction facts.

Assessing Students' Knowledge of Subtraction Facts

Do some assessment to help keep track of which subtraction facts still need practice. This can be done individually with students' sets of Subtraction Cards, which they made in Unit 3. In this unit, there will be a final assessment of subtraction facts in 3.4 and 3.5. In the meantime, as students work on subtraction problems, help them relate subtraction expressions to the addition combinations they know.

Fluency Benchmarks for Learning Facts Through the Grades

Addition: fluency by the end of Grade 2 with review and practice in Grade 3

Subtraction: fluency by the end of Grade 3 with review and practice in Grade 4

Multiplication: fluency with combinations with products to 50 by the end of Grade 3; up to 12 × 12 by the end of Grade 4

Division: fluency with division facts by the end of Grade 5

Subtraction Strategies

Students' strategies for subtraction fall into three basic categories: 1) subtracting in parts, 2) adding up or subtracting back, and 3) changing the numbers to numbers that are easier to subtract. In this Grade 3 unit, students are primarily focusing on strategies that fall in the first two categories. The emphasis is on ways to break numbers apart into smaller pieces that can easily be either subtracted or added, and knowing how to combine those pieces to get an accurate solution. In order to use these strategies, students must understand the meaning of subtraction and have a good mental model of what is happening in the problem. They must be able to look at the problem as a whole, think about the relationships of the numbers in the problem, and choose an approach they can carry out easily and accurately.

Here are examples of students' strategies using the following problem as an example:

$$251 - 187 =$$

Subtracting in Parts

$$251 - 187 =$$
$$251 - 100 = 151$$
$$151 - 80 = 71$$
$$71 - 7 = 64$$

$$\begin{array}{r} 251 \\ -\ 100 \\ \hline 151 \\ -\ 50 \\ \hline 101 \\ -\ 30 \\ \hline 71 \\ -\ 7 \\ \hline 64 \end{array}$$

These two students subtracted 187 in parts. The first student broke up 187 by place (100, 80, 7), while the second student subtracted 100 first, and then broke the 87 into numbers (50, 30, 7) easier to work with. When

students use this strategy, they should be encouraged to subtract the largest parts they can use, while still making sense of the problem and the numbers.

Adding Up or Subtracting Back

In this category of strategies, students visualize how much more or less one number is than the other, and either "add up" or "subtract back" to find their answer. They often represent the subtraction as the distance between two numbers on a number line. In Set A, students start at 187, and "add up" until they reach 251.

Set A: Adding up

$$251 - 187 =$$

$$187 + \underline{13} = 200 \qquad\qquad 187 + \underline{20} = 207$$
$$200 + \underline{51} = 251 \qquad\qquad 207 + \underline{40} = 247$$
$$13 + 51 = 64 \qquad\qquad 247 + \underline{4} = 251$$
$$\qquad\qquad\qquad\qquad\qquad 20 + 40 + 4 = 64$$

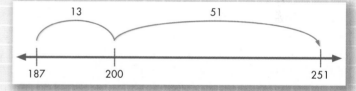

Both students thought of the solution as how much more must be added to 187 to get a sum of 251. Implicitly, they are using the inverse relationship of addition and subtraction to solve the problem. As shown on the number line, the first student added 13 to 187 to get to 200, then added 51 to get to 251. The second student added multiples of 10 to get very close to 251, then added on the final 4.

Set B: Subtracting Back

In this set of solutions, students started at 251, and then "subtracted back" until they reached 187.

$$251 - \underline{51} = 200$$
$$200 - \underline{13} = 187$$
$$51 + 13 = 64$$

$$
\begin{array}{r}
251 \\
- \ 51 \\
\hline
200 \\
- \ 10 \\
\hline
190 \\
- \ 3 \\
\hline
187
\end{array}
$$

$$51 + 10 + 3 = 64$$

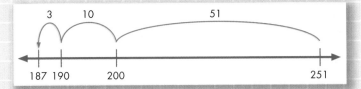

Both students solved the problem by "going back" to 200 and then "back 13 more" to 187. As you can see, in the number line representations, students are not subtracting 187 in parts as in the first category; rather, they start at 251 and subtract until they reach 187, then determine how much they subtracted.

Changing the Numbers

In this category of strategies, students change one or both of the numbers to what they often call "landmark" or "friendly" numbers. In the following examples, students changed one or both of the numbers, subtracted, then compensated for the changes they had made.

$$251 - 187 =$$

$$251 - 200 = 51 \qquad\qquad 250 - 200 = 50$$
$$51 + 13 = 64 \qquad\qquad 50 + 14 = 64$$

The first student changed 187 to 200 to create an easier subtraction problem. Since the student had subtracted 13 too much, 13 was then added to 51 to get the final answer. The second student changed both numbers and had to decide how both those changes affected the result. Since the difference between the two numbers was decreased by 1 (changing 251 to 250) and by 13 (changing 187 to 200), 14 is added to 50. Visualizing the effect of the changes and, therefore, how to compensate for those changes, is critical to this kind of strategy. Changing both numbers as in this second strategy is not easily understood by most third graders. However, changing one number is a strategy that some third graders can use effectively. Number lines are particularly useful tools for visualizing how changing numbers affects the result.

Another strategy in this category is to change both numbers in order to create an equivalent problem that can then be solved without any need to compensate for changes. For example, rather than adding 13 at the end in the first solution above, 13 is added both to 187 and to 251, which maintains the difference between the two numbers ($251 - 187 = 264 - 200$). Students will have an opportunity to explore this strategy further in later grades.

At the end of Grade 3, students should feel comfortable and confident with at least one strategy for subtraction with 3-digit numbers, and be using it with some efficiency—working with larger parts of the numbers and combining steps in their solutions.

Assessment: Subtraction Strategies

Problem 2

Benchmark addressed:

Benchmark 4: Solve subtraction problems with 3-digit numbers using strategies that involve either subtracting a number in parts, adding up, or subtracting back.

In order to meet the benchmark, students' work should show that they can:

- Use one of the following subtraction strategies accurately:

  - Subtract one number in parts, using "chunks" of the number of reasonable size

  - Add up from the smaller number to the larger number, using multiples of 10 or 100 as "stopping-off places" (e.g., $348 + 2 = 350$, $350 + 50 = 400$, and so on)

  - Subtract back from the larger number to the smaller number, using multiples of 10 or 100 as "stopping-off places" (e.g., $436 - 36 = 400$, $400 - 50 = 350$, and so on)

- Record their strategies clearly, using addition or subtraction notation and/or a number line representation.

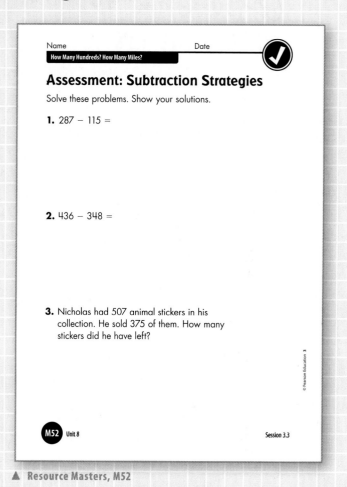

▲ **Resource Masters, M52**

Meeting the Benchmark

Students who meet the benchmark demonstrate that they can choose one of the strategies that they have been working with and discussing, use the strategy accurately, and record their thinking clearly.

Keisha subtracts 348 in parts. Her notation is unusual in that she strings successive subtractions together in one long equation. However, it is clear that she has made use of all of the parts of 348, and she jots down the result of each subtraction accurately.

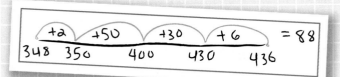

$$436 - 300 - 6 - 2 - 40 = 88$$
$$136 \qquad 130 \quad 128$$

Keisha's Work

Beatriz adds up from 348 to 436 on a number line, stopping at multiples of 10 and 100 along the way.

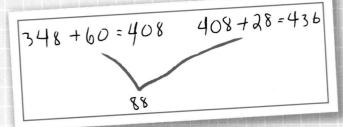

$+2 \quad +50 \quad +30 \quad +6 \quad = 88$
348 350 400 430 436

Beatriz's Work

Nicholas also adds up. He demonstrates that he is able to add multiples of 10 to multidigit numbers. He appears to use the multiple of 100 (400) as a landmark, choosing to add up 60 from 348, even though he does not land on 400 exactly.

$$348 + 60 = 408 \qquad 408 + 28 = 436$$
$$88$$

Nicholas's Work

Arthur subtracts back from 436 to 348 and combines the partial differences to get his solution. He shows his work with both a number line and equations. Note that on Arthur's number line, he places the higher number on the left, rather than the right.

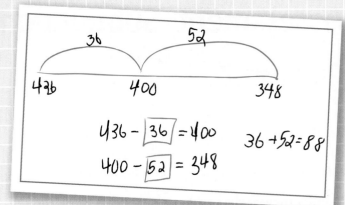

36   52
436   400   348

$$436 - \boxed{36} = 400 \qquad 36 + 52 = 88$$
$$400 - \boxed{52} = 348$$

Arthur's Work

Jung uses a strategy that combines subtracting in parts and changing one of the numbers and then adjusting. She first subtracts 348 in parts from 400 and then recognizes that she must add back the rest of 436, which she also does in place-value parts. She keeps track of the parts of both numbers, crossing out each part as she uses it.

$$\cancel{400} + \cancel{30} + \cancel{6} - \cancel{300} + \cancel{40} + \cancel{8}$$
$$436 - 348$$
$$400 - 300 = 100$$
$$100 - 40 = 60$$
$$60 - 8 = 52$$
$$52 + 30 = 82$$
$$82 + 6 = 88$$

Jung's Work

Partially Meeting the Benchmark

Some students may have a solid understanding of subtraction with 3-digit numbers but may either incorrectly complete the computation, lose track of some part of the problem after they have broken the numbers apart, or use an accurate but inefficient solution that does not make use of multiples of 10. When students' work shows incorrect computation, ask whether they have double-checked their work. Determine whether these are simply errors or whether, for example, the student needs to review some subtraction facts or another aspect of subtraction, such as subtracting multiples of 10.

Kim writes equations that show the difference between each number in the problem and 400. However, she incorrectly computes $348 + 53 = 400$ and comes up with an answer of 89 instead of 88.

$$348 + 53 = 400$$
$$400 + 36 = 436$$
$$53 + 36 = 89$$

Kim's Work

Not Meeting the Benchmark

Some students may not yet have one subtraction strategy that they can use accurately. For example, Murphy attempted to use the U.S. standard algorithm for subtraction. Because he does not understand the reasoning behind the algorithm, he made the common mistake of subtracting the smaller digit from the larger digit in each column, regardless of which number those digits are in.

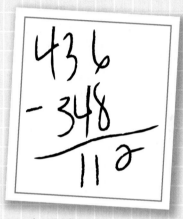

$$436$$
$$- 348$$
$$\overline{112}$$

Murphy's Work

These students will need to continue to practice a strategy that is most accessible to them, which in many cases is likely to be the strategy of subtracting the smaller number in place-value parts. Continue to model this strategy for these students and provide opportunities to practice it. After students have gained proficiency with the strategy you choose to have them practice, suggest that they try variations, such as different ways to break the numbers apart.

Teacher Note

Reasoning and Proof in Mathematics

As students find strategies to perform calculations, they frequently make claims about numerical relationships. Part of the work in Grade 3 involves helping students strengthen their ability to verbalize those claims and consider such questions as: Does this claim hold for *all* numbers? How can we know? Finding ways to answer these questions provides the basis for making sense of formal proof when it is introduced years from now. Consider the following vignette in which a third-grade class is discussing the solution for 650 − 596.

Ines: When I did 650 − 596, I thought about the number line. It is 50 back to 600, and then 4 more, so it's 54.

Gil: I used the number line too, but I started at 596 and figured that it is 4 to 600 and then 50 more. I also got 54.

Oscar: I tried to do it with a strategy I use all the time for adding—make a simpler problem. I changed the 596 to 600 because 600 is easy to work with. I added 4 to the 96, so I took away the 4 from the 650 and made it 646. But when you do that, it is not right, because I get 646 − 600 or 46. I see from what Ines and Gil did that it should be 54, but what's wrong with what I did?

Teacher: Maybe the number line will help us see how to adjust Oscar's strategy. Look at 650 − 596 and think about changing the 596 by adding 4 to make it 600. Is there a way to use that approach and get the right answer, 54?

Gil: If you start at 600 instead of 596, you would have to go past 650 in order to have it be the same. Wait, you would have to go 4 more. That would be 654.

Teacher: Are you saying that 654 − 600 would be the same as 650 − 596?

Ines: Yes. I see it now. If the 596 goes up by 4, you have to make the 650 go up by 4 too.

Oscar: Will that work all the time—I mean, adding the same thing to both numbers in subtraction?

Teacher: Oscar, that is the question I was going to ask. Are we saying that this *always* works—that when you have a subtraction problem, you can change both numbers by some amount and still get the same answer? Can you say exactly what you are doing?

Ines: I am not sure, but I think so. If you add the same thing to both numbers, the answer won't change.

Teacher: We have an example of what Ines is saying: 650 − 596 = 654 − 600. We have been using number lines, story contexts, and paper clip boxes as tools for helping us think about math problems. Can we find a way to use these tools to show what is happening and why it has to stay the same answer? You might want to begin with the examples we have seen, but you also have to show how your argument will work for *all* numbers.

In this class, Ines made an assertion—mathematicians call such an assertion a *conjecture*—that the difference of two numbers remains the same if you add the same quantity to both numbers in a subtraction problem. The teacher has challenged the class to find a way to show that this conjecture is true not just for the examples they have noted but for *all* pairs of numbers. If they can find a proof, they have what mathematicians call a *theorem* or *proposition*.

Let us return to the classroom to see how the third-graders responded to their teacher's challenge to justify their conjecture.

Pilar: I thought about the paper clips. If one person has 650 paper clips and another has only 596 and I give them both 4 more, the person who had the most before has the most still. That doesn't change, because I gave them the same amount. Whatever the difference was before, it is the same.

Nicholas: You can see that on the number line too. If I first think of 650 − 596, it is this much. (Nicholas holds his fingers apart to show the difference between 650 and 596 on the number line.) If I keep my fingers this far apart and move up 4 from 596 so I start at 600, that makes the other finger land at 654. They are the same amount apart still.

Teacher: Pilar used the paper clip model and Nicholas used the number line. They help us see how 650 − 596 = 654 − 600, but how does that show you can *always* do this no matter what the subtraction problem is?

Pilar: It really doesn't matter what the numbers are. If one person has more to begin with and you give them both the same amount, that person still has the same amount more.

Nicholas: On the number line, no matter what problem I start with, it doesn't matter. I just move both numbers up by the same amount and so the space between them will have to be the same.

Students in grades K−5 can work productively on developing justifications for mathematical ideas, as Pilar and Nicholas do here. But what is necessary to justify an idea in mathematics? First, we will examine what proof is in the field of mathematics, and then return to what kind of proving students can do in Grade 3.

What Is Proof in Mathematics?

Throughout life, when people make a claim or assertion, they are often required to justify the claim, to persuade others that it is valid. A prosecutor who claims that a person is guilty of a crime must make an argument, based on evidence, to convince the jury of this claim. A scientist who asserts that the Earth's atmosphere is becoming warmer must marshal evidence, usually in the form of data and accepted theories and models, to justify the claim. Every field, including the law, science, and mathematics, has its own accepted standards and rules for how a claim must be justified in order to persuade others.

When K−5 students are asked to give reasons why their mathematical claims are true, they often say things such as "It worked for all numbers we could think of." "I kept on trying and it kept on working." "We asked the sixth-graders and they said that it was true," or "We asked our parents." These are appeals to particular instances and to authority. In any field, there are appropriate times to turn to authority (a teacher or a book, for example) for help with new knowledge or with an idea that we do not yet have enough experience to think through for ourselves. Similarly, particular examples can be very helpful in understanding some phenomenon. However, neither an authoritative statement nor a set of examples is sufficient to prove a mathematical assertion about an infinite class (say, all whole numbers).

In mathematics, a *theorem* must start with a mathematical assertion, which has explicit hypotheses (or "givens") and an explicit conclusion. The proof of the theorem must show how the conclusion follows logically from the hypotheses. A mathematical argument is based on logic and gives a sense of why a proposition is true. For instance, the third-graders asserted that the difference of two numbers remains the same if you add the same amount to both numbers. In later years, their theorem might be stated as follows: If $a - b = c$, then $(a + n) - (b + n) = c$. The proof of this claim consists of a series of steps in which one begins with the hypothesis $a - b = c$ and follows a chain of logical deductions ending with the conclusion $(a + n) - (b + n) = c$. Each deduction must be justified by an accepted definition, fact, or principle, such as the commutative or associative property of addition.

The model for such a proof was first established by Euclid, who codified what was known of ancient Greek geometry in his *Elements,* written about 300 B.C.E. In his book, Euclid begins with the basic terms of geometry and, through hundreds of propositions and proofs, moves to beautiful and surprising theorems about geometric figures. What is remarkable is that, in each mathematical realm, you can get so far with such simple building blocks.

What Does Proof Look Like in Third Grade?

One does not expect the rigor or sophistication of a formal proof or the use of algebraic symbolism from young children. Even for a mathematician, precise validation is often developed *after* new mathematical ideas have been explored and are more solidly understood. When mathematical ideas are evolving and there is a need to communicate the sense of *why* a claim is true, then informal means of justification are appropriate. Such a justification can include the use of visual displays, concrete materials, or words. The test of the effectiveness of such a justification is this: Does it rely on logical thinking about the mathematical relationships, rather than on the fact that one or a few specific examples work?

This informal approach to mathematical justification is particularly appropriate in K–5 classrooms, in which mathematical ideas are generally "under construction" and in which sense-making and diverse modes of reasoning are valued. Pilar's argument offers justification for the claim that if you add an amount to both numbers in a subtraction problem, the difference remains the same. The story context of the paper clips illustrates how adding the same amount to each person's collection does not change the difference between the amounts. The result of subtracting one number from another can be represented by the distance between the numbers on the number line. Nicholas shows how the space between the new numbers is the same as the distance between the original numbers.

An important part of Pilar's and Nicholas's justifications is their statements that it does not matter what numbers they begin with. The process they describe with the paper clip and number line models will guarantee that the difference between the numbers remains the same. The arguments Pilar and Nicholas make do not depend on adding exactly 4 to both numbers; these arguments would be the same for adding 5 or 6 or any other number.

It is important to note that when students make such claims of generality—*this is true for all numbers*—"all numbers" refers to the numbers they are using. In this vignette, Pilar's reasoning about subtraction takes place in the context of whole numbers. Pilar and her classmates will need to revisit this argument when the domain of numbers they are working with expands beyond whole numbers.

To support the kind of reasoning illustrated in the vignette, encourage students to use representations (for example, the paper clip context, diagrams, or number lines) to explain their thinking. The use of representations offers a reference for the student who is explaining his or her reasoning, and it also allows more classmates to follow that reasoning. If it seems that students may be thinking only in terms of specific numbers, ask, "Will that work for other numbers? How do you know? Will the explanation be the same?"

End-of-Unit Assessment

Problem 1

Benchmark addressed:

Benchmark 2: Solve 3-digit addition problems using at least one strategy efficiently.

In order to meet the benchmark, students' work should show that they can:

- Use at least one of the following addition strategies accurately and efficiently:

  – Break the numbers apart, either by place value or by making use of reasonable-sized "chunks" of the number, and recombine them accurately

  – Change the numbers to numbers that are easier to add and adjust for the change accurately

- Keep track of all parts of the problem and record their solution clearly, using addition notation.

Name _____ Date _____ ✔

How Many Hundreds? How Many Miles?

End-of-Unit Assessment (page 1 of 2) ✏

Use this information to solve the problems.

Benjamin got $10.00 from his grandmother and went shopping. He bought the following items:

Paperback book	$2.99	Pencil	?
Baseball cards	$1.56	Rubber frog	?
Fruit snack	$1.78	Total	$8.21

1. How much did Benjamin spend on the first three items he bought?

▲ **Resource Masters, M54**

Meeting the Benchmark

Students who meet the benchmark demonstrate that they can choose one of the addition strategies they have been working with and discussing in this unit, use the strategy accurately, and record their thinking clearly. Because this problem involves adding more than two addends, students are likely to combine elements of more than one type of strategy and should be looking for ways to combine the numbers or parts of the numbers efficiently. For example, one of the numbers ($2.99) can easily be changed to a whole dollar amount, so some strategies will make use of this idea. Students may also use a strategy that does not change any numbers, such as adding by place value. The goal is for students to have at least one strategy that they can always use with any 3-digit addition problem by the end of Grade 3.

Note that although this problem (and the other problems in this assessment) involves money amounts, using money notation consistently when students write out the steps to their solutions is not part of this unit's benchmarks. This notation will have greater emphasis in Grade 4, when students do more work with decimals.

Jung began by changing $2.99 to 300. First she added 156 and then added on 178 in place-value parts. She finished by subtracting the 1 that she had added originally to change 299 to 300.

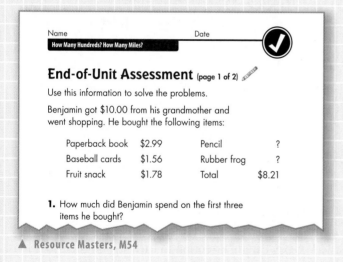

$$300 + 156 = 456$$
$$456 + 100 = 556$$
$$556 + 70 = 626$$
$$626 + 8 = 634$$
$$634 - 1 = 633$$

$6.33

Jung's Work

Becky used a place-value strategy, as she almost always does. She used vertical notation and kept track of each part of the problem as she added.

$$200 \quad 90 \diagdown 140 \qquad\qquad 9$$
$$100 \quad 50 \diagup \qquad\qquad 6 \diagdown 14$$
$$100 \quad 70 \quad 140+60=200 \quad 8 \diagdown$$
$$\overline{400} \quad \overline{210} \qquad\qquad\qquad \overline{23}$$

$$400+210+23=633$$

Becky's Work

Dwayne began by changing the first two numbers to 300 + 155. He has demonstrated in the past that he thinks of this step as "giving 1" from, in this case, 156 to 299. He then added 178 on in parts, first as 150, then 20, and then 8.

$$\$3.00+\$1.55=\$4.55$$
$$455+150=605$$
$$605+20=625$$
$$625+8=633$$

Dwayne's Work

Partially Meeting the Benchmark

Some students may have a solid understanding of addition with 3-digit numbers but may make a computation error or lose track of some part of their solution. These students partially meet the benchmark. When students' work shows incorrect computation, ask whether they have double-checked their work. Determine whether these are simple errors, such as the student lost track of a step in the procedure, misread a number, or simply made a mistake through inattention, or if the student needs to review a few addition combinations.

Zhang began by adding \$1.56 and \$1.78. He correctly added 56 + 78 by place value but then wrote his answer as \$2.34, somehow losing one of the dollars in the problem along the way. For the rest of his solution, he changed 299 to 300 and correctly subtracted 1 at the end.

$$156+178=234$$
$$50+70=120$$
$$6+8=14$$
$$300+234=534$$
$$534-1=533$$

Zhang's Work

Continue to give these students addition problems to solve in the form of Daily Practice and Homework, encouraging them to pay careful attention to each step in their solutions.

Not Meeting the Benchmark

Some students may not yet have one strategy that they can use accurately. Evidence of this could include adding by counting up in very small chunks (by 10s and/or 1s) and losing track; relying on using a representation such as a number line or 100 grids as the only strategy; or not being able to accurately break 3-digit numbers apart and keep track of the parts. These students will need to continue to practice whichever strategy is most accessible to them, probably breaking the numbers apart by place and recombining them.

Continue to model this strategy for these students, help them visualize what is happening as they add parts of numbers, and provide opportunities for practice so that they gain proficiency with one strategy. Talk through the problem, using an addition context that is familiar to them such as the following "200 of the 247 people in one line have gone into the movie theater, and 600 of the 654 people from the other line have gone into the theater. How many people are left in the first line? In the second line? Which group of people do you want to let in next?"

A few students may not yet have a solid understanding of place value, which makes it difficult to keep track of the value of each part of the numbers when solving an addition problem with multidigit numbers. These students may need to work on representing addition of 2- and 3-digit numbers with a visual model of place value, such as the sticker context. They can also benefit from solving more paper clip problems involving boxes of 100 and from playing a version of the *Capture* game, either on the 300 Chart or on the 301 to 600 Chart.

Problems 2 and 3

Benchmark addressed:

Benchmark 4: Solve subtraction problems with 3-digit numbers using strategies that involve either subtracting a number in parts, adding up, or subtracting back.

In order to meet the benchmark, students' work should show that they can:

- Find the difference between $8.21 and $6.33 (the correct solution to Problem 1) by using one of the following subtraction strategies accurately:

  – Subtract one number in parts, using reasonable-sized "chunks" of the number

  – Add up from the smaller number to the larger number, using multiples of 10 or 100 as "stopping-off places"

  – Subtract back from the larger number to the smaller number, using multiples of 10 or 100 as "stopping-off places"

- Record their strategies clearly, using addition or subtraction notation and/or a number line representation.

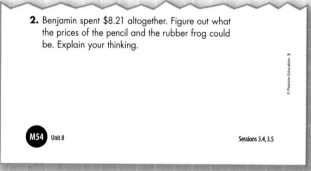

2. Benjamin spent $8.21 altogether. Figure out what the prices of the pencil and the rubber frog could be. Explain your thinking.

© Pearson Education 3

M54 Unit 8   Sessions 3.4, 3.5

▲ Resource Masters, M54

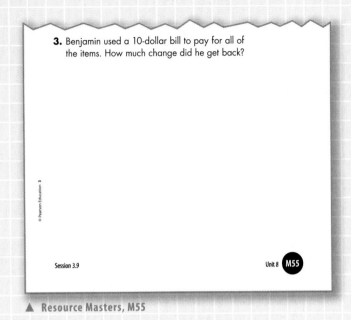

3. Benjamin used a 10-dollar bill to pay for all of the items. How much change did he get back?

© Pearson Education 3

Session 3.9   Unit 8 **M55**

▲ Resource Masters, M55

Meeting the Benchmark

Students who meet the benchmark demonstrate that for each of these problems, they can choose one of the subtraction strategies they have been working with and discussing in this unit, use the strategy accurately, and record their thinking clearly. For Problem 2, students should also be able to accurately separate the difference between $8.21 and $6.33 into two parts that represent the missing prices in the problem. Although this part of the problem does not directly address a benchmark for this unit, it demonstrates students' flexibility in using both addition and subtraction in a variety of problem-solving contexts.

Oscar began by subtracting 600 from 821. He then subtracted 3 to get 218. In order to find the solution to $218 - 30$, he wrote a series of three related problems: $220 - 30$, $219 - 30$, and $218 - 30$. Oscar decided that the pencil would cost 1 dollar and the rubber frog would cost 88 cents.

$$821 - 600 = 221$$
$$221 - 3 = 218$$
$$218 - 30 =$$
$$220 - 30 = 190$$
$$219 - 30 = 189$$
$$218 - 30 = 188$$

Oscar's Work

Beatriz drew a number line to show how she added up from $6.33 to $8.21. She decided that the pencil would cost $0.98 and the rubber frog would cost $0.90.

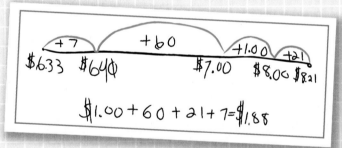

Beatriz's Work

Note that if students have an incorrect answer for Problem 1, as Zhang did, but then use that result correctly in solving Problems 3 and 4, they have met Benchmark 4.

Partially Meeting the Benchmark

Some students may have a solid understanding of subtraction with 3-digit numbers, but either incorrectly complete the computation, lose track of some part of the problem once they have broken the numbers apart, or use an accurate but inefficient solution that does not make use of multiples of 10. When students' work shows incorrect computation, ask if they have double-checked their work. Determine whether these are simply errors, or if, for example, the student needs to review some subtraction facts or another aspect of subtraction, such as subtracting multiples of 10.

For Problem 3, Chris accurately subtracted back from $10.00 to $8.21; however, when he reached 850, his number line shows individual jumps of 10s and 1s, rather than more efficient jumps of 20 and 9. He also does not combine his jumps to say what the final answer is.

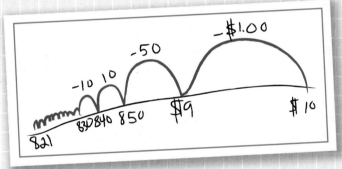

Chris's Work

It is possible that relying on the number line is getting in the way for Chris, considering that he probably knows that the difference between 30 and 21 is 9 without having to count back by 1s. Students like Chris should be encouraged to make their strategies and their notation more concise and efficient. Students who are using number lines exclusively should be encouraged to notate their steps as well. Although use of the number line will continue as a representation in Grade 4, students will also be expected to notate any subtraction strategy with either equations or vertical notation.

Not Meeting the Benchmark

Some students may not yet have one subtraction strategy that they can use accurately. Evidence of this includes answers that are not reasonable or strategies in which numbers are broken apart and subtracted arbitrarily. (An example of this for $8.21 − $6.33 might be to subtract 6 dollars from 8 dollars to get 2 dollars, then subtract 21 cents from 33 cents to get 12 cents, and therefore get an answer of $2.12.) Determine whether this is related to the size of the numbers and, if necessary, give students subtraction problems with 2-digit and small 3-digit numbers for practice.

As with addition, you may need to model a particular strategy. Which strategy you choose may depend on how students visualize the action of subtraction problems. Do some contexts and representations seem more accessible than others? For example, if students can make better sense of the context of traveling from one place to another than of removing large chunks of an amount, they may continue to use a number line and add up as a primary strategy. Such students may also practice subtracting in place-value parts as their primary strategy, using a sticker model. Continue to provide practice for these students throughout the rest of Grade 3, using Daily Practice and Homework activities, keeping in mind that the goal is to leave Grade 3 with at least one subtraction strategy that they can always use.

I Know It's Either 2 More or 2 Less

In Session 1.4, these students are considering the relationship between two subtraction expressions. First they compare 200 − 75 and 200 − 78 and then 350 − 300 and 350 − 298. Although some students may use such relationships to make it easier to solve certain subtraction problems (e.g., thinking of 350 − 298 as 350 − 300 + 2), the primary purpose of this discussion is not to help students use this method for subtraction. Rather, by considering these pairs of subtraction expressions, students have to think hard about how the operation of subtraction works and what each number means.

The class is considering this story problem.

> Deondra had two boxes of paper clips and used 75 of them to make a wire sculpture. Arthur had two boxes of paper clips and used 78 of them to make a wire sculpture. Who had more paper clips left?

Teacher: First, what expression can we write for Deondra's paper clips? What about for Arthur's paper clips?

The teacher takes students' suggestions and writes the two expressions on the board.

> Deondra's paper clips: 200 − 75
>
> Arthur's paper clips: 200 − 78

Teacher: So after Deondra uses 75 and Arthur uses 78 clips, who has more left, and how do you know?

Kim: Deondra does, because they had the same amount to begin with, and Deondra didn't use up as many.

Gil: Arthur used up 3 extra. I thought about it like this— they both used 75 at first, so then they would have the same left. But then Arthur used up 3 more, but Deondra didn't use any more.

Teacher: Will this always be true? What if I used different numbers? Let's say that they both start with 350 paper clips. This time, Deondra uses up 300 and Arthur uses 298.

> Deondra's paper clips: 350 − 300
>
> Arthur's paper clips: 350 − 298

Teacher: I know that you know right away how many paper clips Deondra has left. Can you use that answer to help you figure out how many Arthur has left?

Elena: It would just be 2 different because Deondra has 50 left and Arthur will have, wait . . . I know it's either 2 more or 2 less . . .

Denzel: It has to be 2 more because if you have money in your pocket and you spend more, then you'll have less left.

Keith: If you take away less, you end up with more. It has to be. Can I show you what I mean?

Teacher: Did you have a picture of some kind in mind? [Keith nods yes.] So you have an idea about a picture and Denzel came up with a story about money. Before you share your picture, I'd like everyone to make a picture or think of a story context that helps explain whether Arthur ends up with more or less and why.

After students work for a few minutes in pairs and individually, several students share their ideas. Keith draws this on the board:

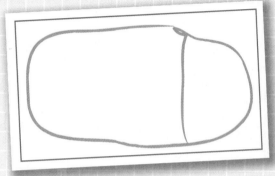

Sample Student Work

Keith: It's like here's a pile of paper clips. You take some away and have some left.

Teacher: Where's the part that you take away, and where's the part that is left?

Keith explains that the larger section represents the 300 clips Deondra uses; the smaller section represents the 50 clips that are left.

Keith: But if you only take away 298, it's over here.

Keith draws a second line, shown by the dotted line below.

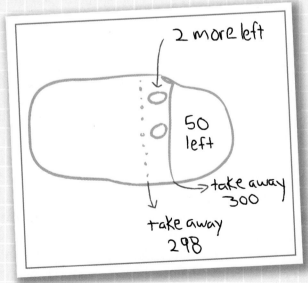

Sample Student Work

Nancy: Yeah, it's like you have this big hunk of bread and you can take a tiny bite or a bigger bite. If you take away smaller you end up with bigger.

Teacher: Did anyone have another way of thinking about it? It was confusing at first. Everyone knew that there was something about a 2, but a lot of people weren't sure if Arthur ends up with 2 more or 2 less. Did anyone come up with another picture or story that helped them think about this?

Ines: I used to think it was 48, but I heard everyone saying it's 52, but I didn't get why. But then when Denzel said about money, me and Kenji thought about 3 dollars and 50 cents. If you spent 3 dollars, you have that 50 cents left, but if you only spent $2.98, you have an extra 2 cents. You'd get 2 cents change from the 3 dollars and you still have 50 cents, so that's 52, not 48.

Even though several students gave clear responses at the beginning of this discussion, the teacher knew that other students needed time to think out and represent these ideas for themselves. By representing their ideas with pictures or by putting them in a context, they are able to think about the meaning of the operation and how the numbers in a subtraction expression are related to each other and to the difference. Underlying what these students are doing are connections between algebra and arithmetic (see **Algebra Connections in This Unit,** page 16).

Are These Equal?

In Session 2.1, this class is discussing one solution to the problem 96 pennies plus 145 pennies, which Keith solved this way:

$$96 \cancel{\text{¢}} + 4 \cancel{\text{¢}} = \$1.00$$

$$\$1.00 + \$1.41 = \$2.41$$

Teacher: Keith, why did you start with one dollar?

Keith: It felt like a good number, and I could just take 4 cents off to make a dollar. If I got to a dollar I thought it would be much more easier.

Teacher: So it's like you changed the problem from 96 pennies plus 145 pennies to an easier problem that had a dollar in it, or 100 pennies.

The teacher writes the following on the board: 96 + 145 = 100 + 141. Then she addresses the whole class.

Teacher: Is this statement true then? Does 96 + 145 = 100 + 141? How do you know?

Elena: It's true because if you figure out the first part, it's 241, and you can see that the second part is 241 too.

Gina: It's just a different way of writing the answer.

Benjamin: If you take the 4 and add it to 96, you get 100 plus 141.

Deondra: The same numbers are on both sides. They're mixed up.

Teacher: Do we have the same amount of pennies on both sides?

Gina: You're just breaking them up into different numbers, and switching them around.

Nicholas: The answer is still 241, either way.

Kenji: They're the same problem, but with different numbers.

Teacher: I'm hearing lots of people prove that both sides are the same answer by figuring them out. So I have a question for you then. What if the numbers were really big, and it would take a long time to solve both problems? Could you still show that both sides were equal, without figuring out the answers?

Ines: You have to go in and find stuff then. Like Keith went looking for 100. He got it from 96 plus 4. If you had, like, 1,000 on one side, you'd have to see if you can find 1,000 on the other side too.

Zhang: It's almost like you built something with all the pennies, and then you wrecked it. And when you put it back together, you have different amounts in each pile. It works as long as you keep the same number of pennies.

The teacher is purposefully pushing students beyond their claim that if they can solve both sides of the problem and get the same solution, they will know that both sides are equal. In this discussion, students are beginning to generalize an idea that is central to the operation of addition, which in algebraic terms can be stated as follows: $a + b = (a + c) + (b - c)$. In his statement at the end, Zhang is beginning to develop a visual image of what is happening mathematically in the equation 96 + 145 = 100 + 141, which can then be applied to other equivalent addition expressions. In the next part of the session, the teacher will ask students to make representations or create story situations that help them better ground their ideas in visual images.

Student Math Handbook

The *Student Math Handbook* pages related to this unit are pictured on the following pages. This book is designed to be used flexibly: as a resource for students doing classwork, as a book students can take home for reference while doing homework and playing math games with their families, and as a reference for families to better understand the work their children are doing in class.

When students take the *Student Math Handbook* home, they and their families can discuss these pages together to reinforce or enhance students' understanding of the mathematical concepts and games in this unit.

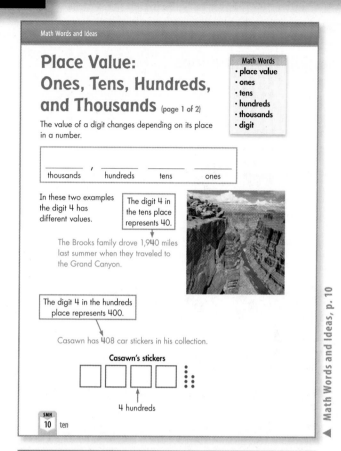

Place Value: Ones, Tens, Hundreds, and Thousands (page 1 of 2)

Math Words
- place value
- ones
- tens
- hundreds
- thousands
- digit

The value of a digit changes depending on its place in a number.

thousands	hundreds	tens	ones

In these two examples the digit 4 has different values.

The digit 4 in the tens place represents 40.

The Brooks family drove 1,940 miles last summer when they traveled to the Grand Canyon.

The digit 4 in the hundreds place represents 400.

Casawn has 408 car stickers in his collection.

Casawn's stickers

4 hundreds

SMH 10 ten

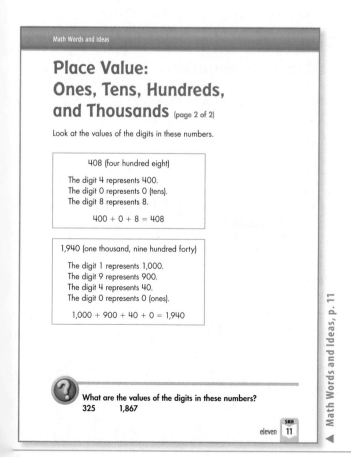

Place Value: Ones, Tens, Hundreds, and Thousands (page 2 of 2)

Look at the values of the digits in these numbers.

> 408 (four hundred eight)
>
> The digit 4 represents 400.
> The digit 0 represents 0 (tens).
> The digit 8 represents 8.
>
> 400 + 0 + 8 = 408

> 1,940 (one thousand, nine hundred forty)
>
> The digit 1 represents 1,000.
> The digit 9 represents 900.
> The digit 4 represents 40.
> The digit 0 represents 0 (ones).
>
> 1,000 + 900 + 40 + 0 = 1,940

? **What are the values of the digits in these numbers?**
325   1,867

eleven **SMH 11**

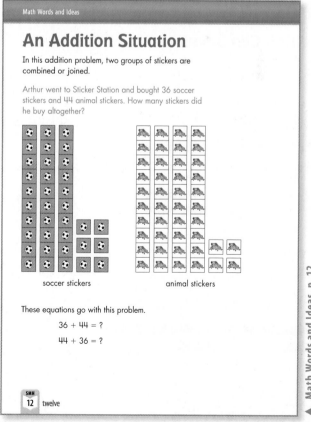

An Addition Situation

In this addition problem, two groups of stickers are combined or joined.

Arthur went to Sticker Station and bought 36 soccer stickers and 44 animal stickers. How many stickers did he buy altogether?

soccer stickers   animal stickers

These equations go with this problem.

$$36 + 44 = ?$$

$$44 + 36 = ?$$

SMH 12 twelve

Math Words and Ideas

Addition Combinations

Math Words
• sum

(page 1 of 4)

One of your goals in math class this year is to review and practice all the addition combinations up to 10 + 10.

10 + 10 =
2 + 7 =
7 + 2 =
3 + 3 =
4 + 6 =
6 + 4 =
5 + 8 =
8 + 5 =

Learning Two Combinations at a Time

These two problems look different, but they have the same sum.

8   +   3   3   +   8

When you know that 8 + 3 = 11, you also know that 3 + 8 = 11.

You've learned two addition combinations!

? Why do these two problems have the same answer?
7 + 2 = 9   2 + 7 = 9

SMH **16** sixteen

◀ Math Words and Ideas, p. 16

Math Words and Ideas

Addition Combinations

(page 2 of 4)

A helpful way to learn addition combinations is to think about one category at a time. Here are some categories you may have seen before. You probably already know many of these combinations.

Make 10 Combinations

2 + 8 = 10   3 + 7 = 10   4 + 6 = 10
8 + 2 = 10   7 + 3 = 10   6 + 4 = 10

Doubles Combinations

6 + 6 = 12   7 + 7 = 14   8 + 8 = 16

Plus 10 Combinations

4 + 10 = 14   5 + 10 = 15   6 + 10 = 16
10 + 4 = 14   10 + 5 = 15   10 + 6 = 16

seventeen SMH **17**

◀ Math Words and Ideas, p. 17

Math Words and Ideas

Addition Combinations

(page 3 of 4)

Here are some more categories to help you learn more of the addition combinations.

Near-Doubles Combinations

Some combinations are close to a doubles combination you know. Here are two examples.

Doubles minus 1	Doubles plus 1
6 + 7 = 7 + 6 =	7 + 8 = 8 + 7 =
Think: 7 + 7 − 1	Think: 7 + 7 + 1
	+1
−1	
7 + 6 = (7 + 7) − 1 = **13**	7 + 8 = (7 + 7) + 1 = **15**

Plus 9 Combinations

You can learn some combinations by relating them to a plus 10 combination you know. Here are two examples.

5 + 9 = 9 + 5 =	
Think: 9 + 1 + 4	Think: 10 + 5 − 1
	−1
9 + 5 = 10 + 4 = **14**	9 + 5 = (10 + 5) − 1 = **14**

SMH **18** eighteen

◀ Math Words and Ideas, p. 18

Math Words and Ideas

Addition Combinations

(page 4 of 4)

As you practice all the addition combinations, there will be some that you "just know" and others that you are "working on." To practice combinations that are difficult for you to remember, think of a combination that you know as a clue to help you.

Here are some examples. Gil and Ines have different clues to help them solve 5 + 7.

Gil: *I think of 7 + 7, and then subtract 2.*

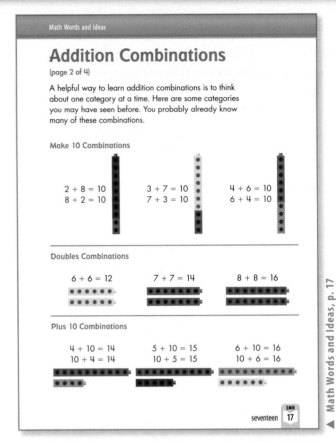

5 + 7 =
7 + 5 =
Clue: 7 + 7 − 2

Ines: *First I add 5 + 5, and then add 2 more.*

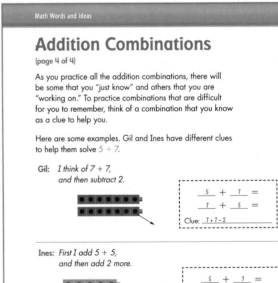

5 + 7 =
7 + 5 =
Clue: 5 + 5 + 2

? Do you know these combinations or are you learning them?

  5   8   7
+7   +6   +4

nineteen SMH **19**

◀ Math Words and Ideas, p. 19

Strategies for Solving Addition Problems (page 1 of 5)

There are different ways to solve addition problems.

Adding by Place

Gina used adding by place to solve this problem.

Bridget went to Sticker Station and bought 46 horse stickers and 74 space stickers. How many stickers did she buy altogether?

Gina's Solution

First I added the tens.	$40 + 70 = 110$
Then, I added the ones.	$6 + 4 = 10$
Then, I put the tens and ones together.	$110 + 10 = \mathbf{120}$

Gina's solution can also be shown using sticker sketches.

46

+ 74

110 + 10 = **120**

I traded 10 strips for a sheet and 10 singles for a strip, so I have 1 sheet and 2 strips.

▲ Math Words and Ideas, p. 20

Strategies for Solving Addition Problems (page 2 of 5)

Ines and Philip used adding by place when they solved this problem.

258
+ 392

They added the hundreds together, the tens together, and the ones together. Their solutions are similar, but they recorded their work differently.

Ines's Solution	Philip's Solution
$200 + 300 = 500$	258
$50 + 90 = 140$	+ 392
	500
$8 + 2 = 10$	140
	+ 10
$500 + 140 + 10 = \mathbf{650}$	650

Ines recorded her solution sideways and Philip recorded his up and down.

How would you solve these problems?

463

37 + 86   + 279

▲ Math Words and Ideas, p. 21

Strategies for Solving Addition Problems (page 3 of 5)

Adding One Number in Parts

Bridget went to Sticker Station and bought 46 horse stickers and 74 space stickers. How many stickers did she buy altogether?

Edwin solved the problem by starting at 74 on the number line and adding 46 in parts.

$46 = 20 + 20 + 6$

Edwin's Solution

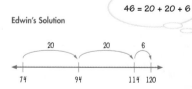

First I added on the 40 from 46 in jumps of 20.	$74 + 20 = 94$
	$94 + 20 = 114$
Then I added the 6.	$114 + 6 = \mathbf{120}$

Is there another way you could solve this problem by adding one number in parts?

▲ Math Words and Ideas, p. 22

Strategies for Solving Addition Problems (page 4 of 5)

258
+ 392

Kenji solved this problem by starting at 258 and adding 392 in parts.

Kenji's Solution

$$392 = 300 + 90 + 2$$

300   90   2

258   558   648 650

First I added the 300.	$258 + 300 = 558$
Then I added the 90.	$558 + 90 = 648$
Then I added the 2.	$648 + 2 = \mathbf{650}$

Benjamin solved this problem by starting at 392 and adding 258 in parts.

Benjamin's Solution

$$258 = 8 + 250$$

8   250

392 400   650

First I added 8.	$392 + 8 = 400$
Then I added 250.	$400 + 250 = \mathbf{650}$

▲ Math Words and Ideas, p. 23

Math Words and Ideas

Strategies for Solving Addition Problems (page 5 of 5)

Changing the Numbers

Bridget went to Sticker Station and bought 46 horse stickers and 74 space stickers. How many stickers did she buy altogether?

Kathryn solved this problem by changing one number.

Kathryn's Solution

I added 4 to 46 to make 50. 50 is a "landmark" number, so it's easier for me to work with.

$46 + 4 = 50$

```
   74
 + 50    I added 50 instead of 46.
  124
 -  4    Then I subtracted the extra 4.
  120
```

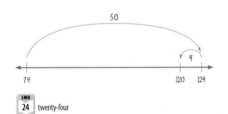

```
           50
    ┌─────────────────┐
                    ┌──┐
                    4
 ──┼─────────────────┼──┼──
   74              120 124
```

◀ Math Words and Ideas, p. 24

Math Words and Ideas

Adding More Than Two Numbers

Here is an addition problem with more than two numbers.

$$139 + 75 + 392$$

Denzel and Elena solved the problem in different ways.

Denzel solved the problem by breaking the numbers apart and adding by place.

Denzel's Solution

```
   139
    75
 + 392
   400   I added the hundreds (100 + 300).
   190   I added the tens (30 + 70 + 90).
 +  16   I added the ones (9 + 5 + 2).
   606   Then I added up the parts to find the total.
```

Elena solved the problem by changing the numbers to make an easier problem to solve.

Elena's Solution

```
131            400   I took 8 from 139 and added it to 392.
139 + 75 + 392       That made the problem
      ⌣ 8            131 + 75 + 400.

131 + 400 = 531   I added the first number and the last number.
531 + 5 = 536     I added 75 in two parts.
536 + 70 = 606
```

 How would you solve this problem?
139 + 75 + 392

◀ Math Words and Ideas, p. 25

Math Words and Ideas

Subtraction Situations

(page 1 of 3)

In Grade 3, you solve subtraction problems involving different types of subtraction situations.

One subtraction situation is *removing*. You solved many removal problems in Grade 2 and will solve more this year.

Removing an Amount

Gina had 165 famous people stickers. She sold 32 of them at a yard sale. How many stickers does Gina have left?

Here are the ways that some students solved this problem.

Elena solved this problem by drawing 165 stickers and crossing out 32 of them. The remaining stickers are the answer.

Elena's Solution

$165 - 32 = $ **133**

Benjamin solved this problem by starting at 165 on the number line and subtracting back 32. The number he landed on is the answer.

Benjamin's Solution

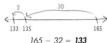

```
         2      30
      ┌──┐┌────────┐
 ──┼──┼──┼─────────┼──
   133 135        165
```

$165 - 32 = $ **133**

 How would you solve this problem?

◀ Math Words and Ideas, p. 26

Math Words and Ideas

Subtraction Situations

(page 2 of 3)

In Grade 3, you also solve subtraction problems involving other types of subtraction situations—finding the unknown part and comparing.

Finding the Unknown Part of a Whole

Last week the Ruiz family drove to Loon Lake. Before leaving home, they set the trip meter of their car to 0. When they stopped for lunch at George's Restaurant, the trip meter read 87 miles. When they reached Loon Lake, the meter read 156 miles. How far did they travel from the restaurant to the lake?

In this subtraction problem, the unknown part is the distance from the restaurant to the lake.

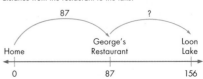

```
         87              ?
    ┌──────────┐   ┌──────────┐
 ──┴──────────┴───┴──────────┴──
 Home       George's        Loon
            Restaurant       Lake
   0            87            156
```

◀ Math Words and Ideas, p. 27

Panel 1 (top-left)

Subtraction Situations

(page 3 of 3)

Comparing Two Amounts

The rainbow snake at the nature center is 53 inches long. The boa constrictor is 84 inches long. How much longer is the boa constrictor?

In this subtraction problem, the lengths of two snakes are compared to find out how much longer one is than the other.

rainbow snake
53 inches long

boa constrictor
84 inches long

◀ Math Words and Ideas, p. 28

Panel 2 (top-right)

Tools to Represent Subtraction Problems (page 1 of 2)

On this page and the next, you will see some of the tools you can use to represent subtraction problems such as this one.

Ms. Santos's class is collecting cans for a recycling project. Their goal is to collect 175 cans. They have collected 63 cans so far. How many more cans do they need to collect to reach their goal?

$$63 + \underline{112} = 175 \text{ or}$$
$$175 - 63 = \underline{112}$$

Sticker Sketch

The answer is 112, the number of stickers that are left.

Number Line

112

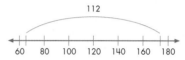

60   80   100   120   140   160   180

The answer is 112, the distance shown on the number line between the numbers 63 and 175.

◀ Math Words and Ideas, p. 29

Panel 3 (bottom-left)

Tools to Represent Subtraction Problems (page 2 of 2)

200 Chart

1	2	3	4	5	6	7	8	9	10
11	12	13	14	15	16	17	18	19	20
21	22	23	24	25	26	27	28	29	30
31	32	33	34	35	36	37	38	39	40
41	42	43	44	45	46	47	48	49	50
51	52	53	54	55	56	57	58	59	60
61	62	(63)	64	65	66	67	68	69	70
71	72	73	74	75	76	77	78	79	80
81	82	83	84	85	86	87	88	89	90
91	92	93	94	95	96	97	98	99	100
101	102	103	104	105	106	107	108	109	110
111	112	113	114	115	116	117	118	119	120
121	122	123	124	125	126	127	128	129	130
131	132	133	134	135	136	137	138	139	140
141	142	143	144	145	146	147	148	149	150
151	152	153	154	155	156	157	158	159	160
161	162	163	164	165	166	167	168	169	170
171	172	173	174	(175)	176	177	178	179	180
181	182	183	184	185	186	187	188	189	190
191	192	193	194	195	196	197	198	199	200

112

Where in each representation on pages 29 and 30 do you see 175? Where in each representation do you see 63? Where in each representation do you see 112?

◀ Math Words and Ideas, p. 30

Panel 4 (bottom-right)

Subtraction Facts Related to Addition Combinations

One of your goals this year is to review and practice all of the addition combinations up to 10 + 10. You can review strategies for practicing the addition combinations on pages 16–19.

Another goal is to learn the subtraction facts related to addition combinations.

Think of the addition combinations that you know when you solve related subtraction problems. Here are some examples.

$$6 + \underline{4} = 10$$

Think:
$10 - 6 = \underline{4}$

10

6   4

$$6 + \underline{9} = 15$$

Think:
$15 - 6 = \underline{9}$

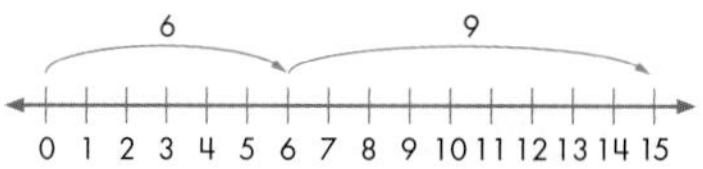

6   9

0 1 2 3 4 5 6 7 8 9 10 11 12 13 14 15

$$8 + \underline{8} = 16$$

Think:
$16 - 8 = \underline{8}$

◀ Math Words and Ideas, p. 31

Math Words and Ideas

Strategies for Solving Subtraction Problems

(page 1 of 4)

Subtraction problems can be solved in different ways.

$$144 - 82 = \underline{\qquad}$$

Adding Up

Bridget solved this problem by adding up. She started at 82 and added up to get to 144. She used 100 as a landmark number.

Bridget's Solution

$82 + \underline{\qquad} = 144$

$82 + \underline{18} = 100$

$100 + \underline{44} = 144$

Bridget: *The answer is the total of the two jumps from 82 to 144.*
18 + 44 = **62**

Subtracting Back

Keith solved the problem by subtracting back. He started at 144 and subtracted back to get to 82.

Keith's Solution

$144 - \underline{\qquad} = 82$

$144 - \underline{4} = 140$

$140 - \underline{40} = 100$

$100 - \underline{10} = 90$

$90 - \underline{8} = 82$

Keith: *The answer is the total of all the jumps from 144 back to 82.*
4 + 40 + 10 + 8 = **62**

 32 thirty-two

▲ Math Words and Ideas, p. 32

Math Words and Ideas

Strategies for Solving Subtraction Problems

(page 2 of 4)

This problem can be solved in different ways.

$$\begin{array}{r} 924 \\ -\ 672 \\ \hline \end{array}$$

Adding Up

Jung solved this problem by starting at 672 and adding up to 924.

Jung's Solution

$672 + \underline{\qquad} = 924$

$672 + \underline{200} = 872$

$872 + \underline{28} = 900$

$900 + \underline{24} = 924$

Jung: *The answer is the total of all the jumps from 672 up to 924.*
200 + 28 + 24 = **252**

Subtracting Back

Gil solved the problem by starting at 924 and subtracting back to 672.

Gil's Solution

$924 - \underline{\qquad} = 672$

$924 - \underline{24} = 900$

$900 - \underline{200} = 700$

$700 - \underline{28} = 672$

Gil: *The answer is the total of all the jumps from 924 back to 672.*
24 + 200 + 28 = **252**

thirty-three **33**

▲ Math Words and Ideas, p. 33

Math Words and Ideas

Strategies for Solving Subtraction Problems

(page 3 of 4)

Subtracting One Number in Parts

$$144 - 82 = \underline{\qquad}$$

Kim solved this problem by starting with 144 and subtracting 82 in parts.

Kim's Solution

I started at 144 on the number line.

I subtracted 40 and landed on 104.   144 − 40 = 104

I subtracted 42 and landed on 62.   102 − 42 = 62

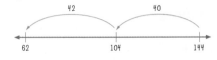

The answer is the number where I ended. 144 − 82 = **62**

 34 thirty-four

▲ Math Words and Ideas, p. 34

Math Words and Ideas

Strategies for Solving Subtraction Problems

(page 4 of 4)

$$\begin{array}{r} 924 \\ -\ 672 \\ \hline \end{array}$$

Arthur solved this problem by starting with 924 and subtracting 672 in parts.

Arthur's Solution

I started at 924.

I subtracted 600 and landed on 324.   924 − 600 = 324

I subtracted 20 and landed on 304.   324 − 20 = 304

I subtracted 50 and landed on 254.   304 − 50 = 254

Arthur: *Then I subtracted 2 and landed on 252.*   254 − 2 = 252

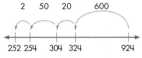

The answer is the number where I landed.   924 − 672 = **252**

 How would you solve these problems?

thirty-five **35**

▲ Math Words and Ideas, p. 35

Adding and Subtracting Tens and Hundreds

When you count by tens, you say the multiples of 10.

10, 20, 30, 40, 50, 60, 70, ...

What happens when you add a multiple of 10 to a number or subtract a multiple of 10 from a number?

Look at what these third-grade students noticed in these problems.

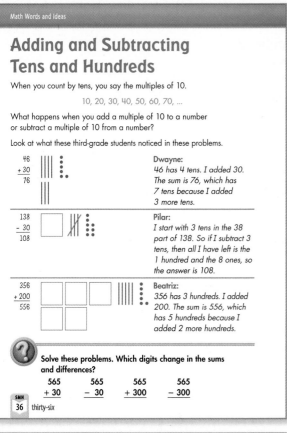

$$\begin{array}{r} 46 \\ + 30 \\ \hline 76 \end{array}$$

Dwayne:
46 has 4 tens. I added 30. The sum is 76, which has 7 tens because I added 3 more tens.

$$\begin{array}{r} 138 \\ - 30 \\ \hline 108 \end{array}$$

Pilar:
I start with 3 tens in the 38 part of 138. So if I subtract 3 tens, then all I have left is the 1 hundred and the 8 ones, so the answer is 108.

$$\begin{array}{r} 356 \\ + 200 \\ \hline 556 \end{array}$$

Beatriz:
356 has 3 hundreds. I added 200. The sum is 556, which has 5 hundreds because I added 2 more hundreds.

Solve these problems. Which digits change in the sums and differences?

$$\begin{array}{r} 565 \\ + 30 \end{array} \quad \begin{array}{r} 565 \\ - 30 \end{array} \quad \begin{array}{r} 565 \\ + 300 \end{array} \quad \begin{array}{r} 565 \\ - 300 \end{array}$$

SMH 36 thirty-six

Coin Values and Equivalencies (page 1 of 2)

Math Words
- penny
- nickel
- dime

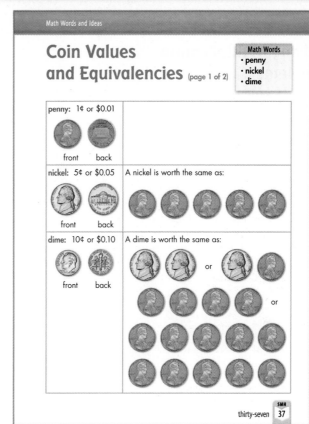

penny: 1¢ or $0.01

front   back

nickel: 5¢ or $0.05 — A nickel is worth the same as:

front   back

dime: 10¢ or $0.10 — A dime is worth the same as:

or

or

thirty-seven **37**

Coin Values and Equivalencies (page 2 of 2)

Math Words
- quarter
- half dollar

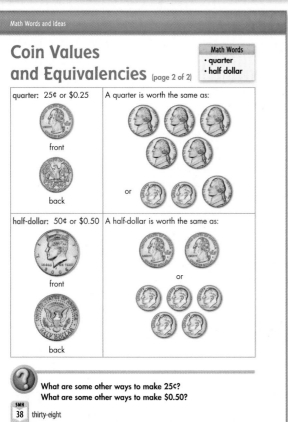

quarter: 25¢ or $0.25 — A quarter is worth the same as:

front

back

or

half-dollar: 50¢ or $0.50 — A half-dollar is worth the same as:

front

or

back

What are some other ways to make 25¢?
What are some other ways to make $0.50?

SMH 38 thirty-eight

Solving Multiplication Problems (page 1 of 2)

How many cans are there?

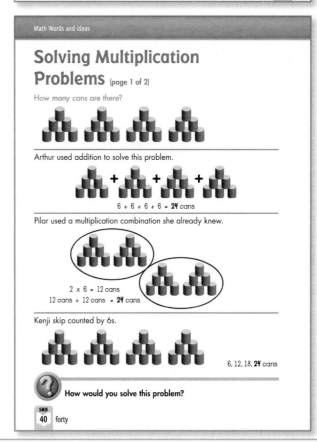

Arthur used addition to solve this problem.

6 + 6 + 6 + 6 = **24** cans

Pilar used a multiplication combination she already knew.

2 × 6 = 12 cans
12 cans + 12 cans = **24** cans

Kenji skip counted by 6s.

6, 12, 18, **24** cans

How would you solve this problem?

SMH 40 forty

Solving Multiplication Problems (page 2 of 2)

There are 5 hexagons.
There are 6 sides on each hexagon.
How many sides are there in all?

$5 \times 6 =$ ____

There are 4 flowers.
There are 5 petals on each flower.
How many petals are there in all?

$4 \times 5 =$ ____

There are 4 boxes of crayons.
There are 3 crayons in each box.
How many crayons are there in all?

CRAYONS CRAYONS CRAYONS CRAYONS

$4 \times 3 =$ ____

How would you solve these problems?

forty-one **SMH 41**

◄ Math Words and Ideas, p. 41

Division

Math Words
· division

Use division when you want to separate a quantity into equal-sized groups.

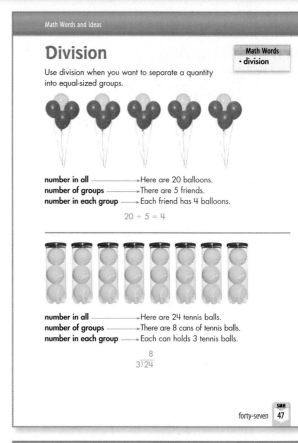

number in all ——————→Here are 20 balloons.
number of groups ————→There are 5 friends.
number in each group ——→Each friend has 4 balloons.

$20 \div 5 = 4$

number in all ——————→Here are 24 tennis balls.
number of groups ————→There are 8 cans of tennis balls.
number in each group ——→Each can holds 3 tennis balls.

$3\overline{)24}$ with 8 above

forty-seven **SMH 47**

◄ Math Words and Ideas, p. 47

Solving Division Problems

Oscar has 24 marbles. He wants to put 4 marbles in a bag. How many bags can Oscar fill?

$24 \div 4 =$ ____ $4\overline{)24}$ ____ $\times 4 = 24$

Here are the ways that some students solved this problem.

Bridget skip counted by 4s. 4, 8, 12, 16, 20, 24 (1), (2), (3), (4), (5), (6) **6** groups	Adam used 24 cubes and made groups of 4. ⊞ ⊞ ⊞ ⊞ ⊞ ⊞ **6** groups of 4
Cristobal used a multiplication combination he already knew. $5 \times 4 = 20$ (5 groups) **6** groups $1 \times 4 = 4$ (1 more group)	Gina used a multiplication combination she already knew. $3 \times 4 = 12$ $3 \times 4 = \underline{12}$ $6 \times 4 = \overline{24}$ **6** groups

Oscar can fill **6** bags.

How would you solve this problem?

SMH 48 forty-eight

◄ Math Words and Ideas, p. 48

Multiplication Combinations (page 1 of 3)

Here are some ways to help you learn the multiplication combinations with products up to 50.

Learning Two Combinations at a Time

5×3 and 3×5

These two problems look different, but they have the same answer.

When you know that $5 \times 3 = 15$, you also know that $3 \times 5 = 15$.

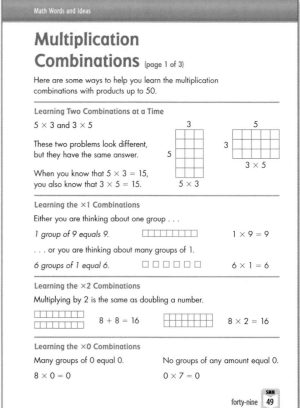

5×3 3×5

Learning the ×1 Combinations

Either you are thinking about one group . . .

1 group of 9 equals 9. $1 \times 9 = 9$

. . . or you are thinking about many groups of 1.

6 groups of 1 equal 6. $6 \times 1 = 6$

Learning the ×2 Combinations

Multiplying by 2 is the same as doubling a number.

$8 + 8 = 16$ $8 \times 2 = 16$

Learning the ×0 Combinations

Many groups of 0 equal 0.   No groups of any amount equal 0.

$8 \times 0 = 0$ $0 \times 7 = 0$

forty-nine **SMH 49**

◄ Math Words and Ideas, p. 49

Math Words and Ideas

Fractions

Math Words
· fraction

Fractions are numbers.

Some fractions, such as $\frac{1}{4}$ and $\frac{1}{2}$, are less than 1.

Some fractions, such as $\frac{2}{2}$ and $\frac{4}{4}$, are equal to 1.

Some fractions, such as $\frac{6}{4}$ and $\frac{3}{2}$, are greater than 1.

Fractions can be used to show parts of a whole.

One third of this flag is white.

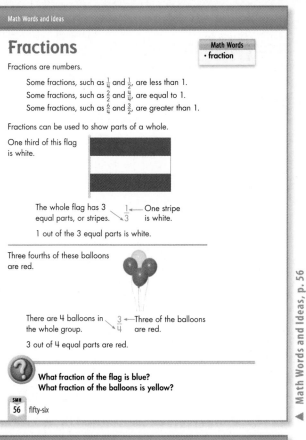

The whole flag has 3 equal parts, or stripes. $\frac{1}{3}$ — One stripe is white.

1 out of the 3 equal parts is white.

Three fourths of these balloons are red.

There are 4 balloons in the whole group. $\frac{3}{4}$ — Three of the balloons are red.

3 out of 4 equal parts are red.

What fraction of the flag is blue?
What fraction of the balloons is yellow?

Math Words and Ideas

Naming Fractions (page 1 of 2)

In each of these examples, one whole rectangle has been divided into equal parts. The part of the rectangle shaded blue and the part of the rectangle shaded yellow are named.

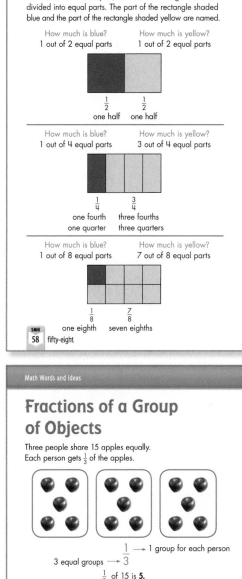

How much is blue?
1 out of 2 equal parts

How much is yellow?
1 out of 2 equal parts

$\frac{1}{2}$ $\frac{1}{2}$
one half   one half

How much is blue?
1 out of 4 equal parts

How much is yellow?
3 out of 4 equal parts

$\frac{1}{4}$ $\frac{3}{4}$
one fourth   three fourths
one quarter   three quarters

How much is blue?
1 out of 8 equal parts

How much is yellow?
7 out of 8 equal parts

$\frac{1}{8}$ $\frac{7}{8}$
one eighth   seven eighths

Math Words and Ideas

Naming Fractions (page 2 of 2)

How much is blue?
1 out of 3 equal parts

How much is yellow?
2 out of 3 equal parts

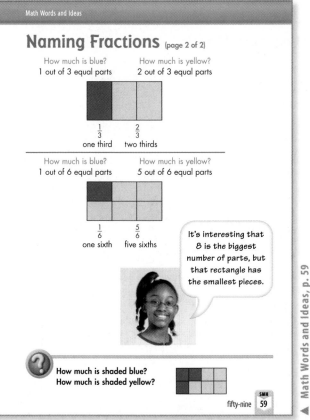

$\frac{1}{3}$ $\frac{2}{3}$
one third   two thirds

How much is blue?
1 out of 6 equal parts

How much is yellow?
5 out of 6 equal parts

$\frac{1}{6}$ $\frac{5}{6}$
one sixth   five sixths

It's interesting that 8 is the biggest number of parts, but that rectangle has the smallest pieces.

How much is shaded blue?
How much is shaded yellow?

Math Words and Ideas

Fractions of a Group of Objects

Three people share 15 apples equally. Each person gets $\frac{1}{3}$ of the apples.

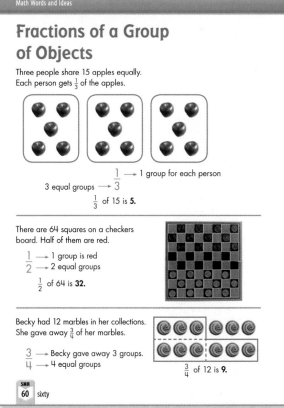

$\frac{1}{3}$ — 1 group for each person

3 equal groups — $\frac{1}{3}$

$\frac{1}{3}$ of 15 is **5.**

There are 64 squares on a checkers board. Half of them are red.

$\frac{1}{2}$ — 1 group is red

$\frac{1}{2}$ — 2 equal groups

$\frac{1}{2}$ of 64 is **32.**

Becky had 12 marbles in her collections. She gave away $\frac{3}{4}$ of her marbles.

$\frac{3}{4}$ — Becky gave away 3 groups.

$\frac{3}{4}$ — 4 equal groups

$\frac{3}{4}$ of 12 is **9.**

Fraction Combinations

These students wrote equations to show the fraction parts and totals for each of these pictures.

Chiang	Keisha
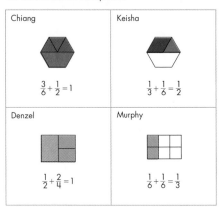 $\frac{3}{6} + \frac{1}{2} = 1$	$\frac{1}{3} + \frac{1}{6} = \frac{1}{2}$
Denzel	Murphy
$\frac{1}{2} + \frac{2}{4} = 1$	$\frac{1}{6} + \frac{1}{6} = \frac{1}{3}$

 Use pattern blocks to find more fraction combinations that equal 1.

Capture from 300 to 600

(page 1 of 2)

You need

- 301–600 chart, taped together
- Plus/Minus Cards
- 30 chips
- game piece for each player
- *Capture from 300 to 600* Recording Sheet

Play in pairs or in 2 teams.

1 Place 30 chips on the 301–600 chart so each chip is on a different number. Deal five Plus/Minus Cards to each player or team and place the remaining cards facedown on the table. Players put their game pieces anywhere on the 301–600 chart to start.

2 Players or teams take turns trying to capture a chip. On your turn, move your game piece using any combination of your Plus/Minus Cards to land on a square with a chip. You can use any number of cards, from one to all five.

3 If you land exactly on a square with a chip, capture it by taking it off the board. You can capture only one chip during a turn, and it must be from the square you land on.

Capture from 300 to 600

(page 2 of 2)

4 Record your moves in an equation on the *Capture from 300–600* Recording Sheet. For example, if you begin on 445 and use the cards +2, +10, −100, and +3, you record 445 + 2 + 10 − 100 + 3 = 360.

5 Find how many spaces you moved altogether, and record that, too. In the example above, you moved forward 15 spaces (+2, +10, and +3) and backward 100 spaces (−100), so altogether you moved backward 85 spaces from 445.

6 Place the Plus/Minus Cards you used facedown in a discard pile. Take cards from the top of the deck to replace them. If the deck of Plus/Minus Cards is used up, shuffle the discard pile and turn it facedown on the table.

7 The first player or team to capture five chips wins.

Collections Match

You need

- deck of Collection Cards
- *Combining Collections: How Many Altogether?*

Play in pairs or in 2 teams.

1 The object is to make matches of Collection Cards from the same category and to find the sum of the two collections in three matches.

2 Lay out 12 Collection Cards facedown on the table, in 3 rows with 4 cards in each row.

3 Take turns turning over two cards from anywhere in the layout. If the two cards are both in the same category, such as dolls, stamps, or trading cards, they are a match and you keep them. If the cards do not match, turn the cards back over and your turn is over.

4 When you collect a match, replace the missing cards with new cards from the deck so that there are always 12 cards to choose from.

5 The player with the most matches when all the cards have been turned over wins the game.

6 When all the cards have been matched, each player chooses three matches to solve for an exact sum. Record the three addition problems on *Combining Collections: How Many Altogether?* and solve each problem.

Games

Count and Compare

You need

- set of Array Cards

Play with a partner or in a small group.

1. Deal the Array Cards so that all players have the same number of cards. Set aside any cards that are left over.

2. Players place their cards in a stack in front of them with the dimensions side up.

3. Each player places the top card from his or her stack, dimension side up, in the middle of the table.

4. Players decide whose card has the largest array by skip counting, using a known multiplication combination, placing the arrays on top of each other, or some other strategy. Counting the squares by 1s is not allowed.

5. The player with the largest array takes all the cards from the round and places them on the bottom of his or her stack. If all arrays in the round have the same product, players make a rule to determine who gets the cards. When a rule is decided, it cannot be changed until the game is over.

Possible rule: Each player places a second card on top of his or her first one. The player with the largest array of all second cards takes all of the first cards and all of the second cards.

6. The game is over when one player runs out of cards. The player with the most cards (or all of the cards) is the winner.

SMH
G9

▲ Games, G9

Index